C000113336

TECTONIC HAZARDS

CAMERON DUNN AND MARTIN DEGG
SERIES EDITORS: BOB DIGBY AND SUE WARN

ISBN 978-1-84377-257-6
First published 2012
Impression number 10 9 8 7 6 5 4 3 2
Year 2014 2013 2012

Published by the Geographical Association, 160 Solly Street, Sheffield S1 4BF
Company number 07139068
Website: www.geography.org.uk
E-mail: info@geography.org.uk
The Geographical Association is a registered charity: no 1135148

The GA would be happy to hear from other potential authors who have ideas for geography books. You may contact the Publications Officer via the GA at the address above.

Cover image: © Beboy_Ltd/iStockphoto
Copy edited by Andrew Shackleton
Cartography/illustrations by Kim Farrington
Designed and typeset by Ledgard Jepson Ltd
Printed and bound in China through Colorcraft Ltd, Hong Kong

Contents

Editors' preface

The *Top Spec Geography* series is designed to be used by 16–19 year olds in schools and colleges. The writing teams, combining the expertise of a specialist in their field with that of an experienced classroom teacher, have been chosen to ensure that contemporary and exciting geography, which brings together the latest research and thinking on topical themes, is accessible to post-16 students.

Each book in the series consists of:
- written chapters, with illustrations and data which complement the text
- activities for use in groups and as guides for private study. Some activities are designed to encourage discussion, while others help to promote students' understanding of the issues
- ideas for further research: most post-16 teaching encourages students to become independent learners and some specifications have research units designed to help prepare students for this
- a glossary of key words and terms.

In addition, there are online resources which have been written to extend and complement the book, and will ensure that the most up-to-date research and data are available. Each chapter will remind you about these resources which can be found at *www.geography.org.uk/topspec.*

Although the books have been written mainly with geography students in mind, the series may also prove useful for students:
- taking public examination or diploma courses in other subjects
- who want to read beyond their exam courses in order to apply or prepare for university
- looking at new topics in their first year of university.

Tectonic Hazards

Tectonic hazards is a very popular topic at GCSE, post 16 and university level. It enthuses countless numbers of students to study the subject further because of its topicality, relevance and ability to link physical and human geography. Many universities have specialist research centres dedicated to risk assessment and hazard event analysis.

After an introduction to hazard and risk, which emphasises the contribution that vulnerability makes to the development of disasters, the book explores the key tectonic processes which are fundamental to our understanding of the geography of tectonic hazards at all scales. These processes, which are broadly divided into seismic and volcanic, are responsible for the development of distinctive landscapes both active and relict.

The section on seismic activity analyses the complex relationship between earthquakes and their impact on human society. It considers why it is that although we have the potential to manage the impacts of earthquakes they continue to be the most costly of natural hazards.

The tsunami hazard is a secondary one resulting from earthquakes or volcanic activity. Although high magnitude tsunami are relatively rare, even with effective prediction and preparedness they can lead to devastating events such that in Japan in 2011.

Volcanoes are rarely a major killer because of their spatial predictability but the diversity of volcanic activity can lead to some major disasters in isolated cases. Geographers have a unique role to play in developing strategies for disaster risk reduction as they can understand the interplay of physical and human factors which put the world at risk.

This book will be useful for all geography A-level specifications most of which have an A2 option on tectonic hazards. It will also be useful for geology students who need to gain a basic understanding of tectonic processes.

Bob Digby and Sue Warn
January 2012

 # Online resources

Each book in the *Top Spec Geography* series has a range of supplementary materials and resources including:
- extra information
- extended question lists
- model answers and mark schemes
- links to relevant websites
- extended glossaries
- photo galleries.

To access these go to *www.geography.org.uk/topspec*, then click on the button for this book. You will then be asked for your password.
The unique password for this book is DD31F6

1. Introducing hazard and risk

Geographers and hazards

Natural hazards are, in essence, a geographical problem, and as such they have enlivened the study of geography for generations, and have enthused countless numbers of students to study the subject to A-level and beyond. Hazards are all about interactions between people and environment, at a variety of spatial and temporal scales, and so no one is better placed than the geographer to make sense of the myriad of social and environmental processes that combine to create hazardous situations. Geologists can study the morphology and stratigraphy of an active or dormant volcano to understand how it formed and how it is likely to behave in the future, while archaeologists, social historians and demographers can tell us things about population changes on and around the same volcano through time. But for a rounded sense of the dynamic interplay between the physical aspects of the volcano and the human processes shaping settlement around it, call for a geographer. Geographers now also have at their disposal powerful spatial mapping and modelling tools, broadly referred to as geographical information systems (GIS), that add a whole new tier of technological sophistication to the contribution that they can make to hazard assessment and disaster management.

From hazard to disaster

The terms hazard and disaster are often used interchangeably, but there is an important distinction between the two – insomuch as the term hazard relates to the *potential* for a particular process to cause loss, whereas disaster is the realisation of that potential. Hence we often talk about a hazardous situation (through which significant losses could occur) as being 'a disaster waiting to happen', but it is not a disaster until the losses actually occur. Hazards can be truly natural, such as an earthquake or volcanic eruption, or quasi-natural (i.e. human-accentuated), such as floods, smog and some aspects of landslides. Information Box 1.1 summarises key hazard and disaster terminology, drawing largely upon UN definitions.

Disasters occur when hazardous processes impact upon populations that are vulnerable, or susceptible, to loss caused by the impact of these processes. Vulnerability is influenced by a very wide range of social, economic, political and environmental factors, and can vary immensely within any given community – and indeed within any given family within a community, as we shall see in many of the chapters in this book. It can be measured in human terms (e.g. susceptibility to death or injury) and/or economic terms (e.g. likelihood of building damage, loss of livelihood, insurance loss). There have been significant advances over the last decade in our understanding of the processes that create conditions of vulnerability (e.g.

INFORMATION BOX 1.1
KEY HAZARD AND RISK TERMINOLOGY

Natural hazard: A potentially damaging physical event that may cause loss of life, property damage, social and economic disruption, or environmental degradation. Natural hazards can be classified by origin, namely: geological, geomorphological, hydrological, meteorological, biological. Hazardous events can vary in magnitude or intensity, frequency, duration, areal extent and speed of onset.

Vulnerability: Susceptibility to loss (deaths, injuries, property, livelihoods, disruption to economic activity or environmental damage) caused by a hazard impact. Conditions of vulnerability are determined by physical, social, economic and environmental factors, or processes that increase the susceptibility of individuals and communities to the impact of particular hazards.

Risk: The probability of harmful consequences or expected losses (see vulnerability) resulting from interactions between natural or human-induced hazards and vulnerable conditions. In its simplest form this relationship is expressed in the pressure and release (PAR) model as Risk (R) = Hazard (H) x Vulnerability (V)

Disaster: The realisation of risk.

Coping capacity/resilience: Coping capacity is the combination of all strengths and resources available within a community or organisation that reduce the level of risk or the effects of a disaster. Resilience describes the capability of a human and/or environmental system to maintain its basic functions and structures in a time of shocks and perturbations (Birkmann, 2006).

Root causes →	Dynamic pressures →	Unsafe conditions	Disaster	Hazards
Limited access to: • power • structures • resources Ideologies: • political systems • economic systems	Lack of: • local institutions • training • appropriate skills • local investments • local markets • press freedom • ethical standards in public life Macro forces: • rapid population growth • rapid urbanisation • arms expenditure • debt repayment schedules • deforestation • decline in soil productivity	Fragile physical environment: • dangerous locations • unprotected buildings and infrastructure Fragile local economy: • livelihoods at risk • low income levels Vulnerable society: • special groups at risk • lack of local institutions Public actions: • lack of disaster preparedness • prevalence of endemic disease	Risk = hazard x vulnerability	Earthquake High winds (cyclone/hurricane/typhoon) Flooding Volcanic eruption Landslide Drought Viruses and pests

Figure 1.1 Model of pressures that create vulnerability and result in disasters. **Source:** after Blaikie *et al.*, 1994, 2004.

Blaikie *et al.*, 1994, 2004; Pelling, 2003). Figure 1.1 shows that it is important to distil the root causes and dynamic pressures that lie behind the surface manifestations of vulnerability (i.e. that cause unsafe conditions). As we shall see in later sections of this book, disaster mitigation efforts have all too frequently focused on the surface manifestations while doing little to tackle the root causes of the problem, often to avoid having to address politically sensitive issues like poverty and unequal access to resources – it is easier to talk about earthquake evacuation drills than it is to talk of empowering people to reduce their vulnerability through social and political change.

In assessing the impact of hazards upon different parts of the world, disaster statistics frequently focus upon the effectiveness of different hazard types in a) killing people and b) causing economic/insurance loss and social disruption. The threshold at which the losses from a hazard impact are considered significant enough to be referred to as a 'disaster' is rather ambiguous, with relatively minor impacts in Western societies frequently being referred to in the media as disasters, while more

major impacts in poorer countries are often largely overlooked by the international community. The United Nations considers 'great natural catastrophes' to be those which kill thousands of people, make hundreds of thousands homeless, cause substantial economic loss, and require interregional or international disaster relief and recovery assistance for the areas affected. Figure 1.2 plots data relating to such events, classified by broad hazard type, for the last 60 years. This figure and related data show that:

• Hydrometeorological hazards (flood, windstorm, drought) have accounted for approximately 70% of great natural catastrophes since 1950, and tectonic hazards (predominantly earthquakes) for about 30%.

• Tectonic hazards have been the deadliest hazard category during this period, and among these earthquakes have been the single greatest killer of people (tsunami have proved particularly deadly in the last 10 years).

• Meteorological hazards (windstorm activity) have accounted for the majority (79%) of insurance loss, primarily through their impact in North America and Western Europe.

• There has been a clear upward trend in the number of disasters recorded since the 1950s (Munich Re, 1999, 2004).

Hazard and vulnerability as components of risk

Projecting forward, risk is the potential for loss when a hazard of a given magnitude and spatial extent impacts upon a population of given vulnerability attributes – in essence it represents a modelling of the loss or disaster potential using hazard and vulnerability as key input variables. In its simplest form this relationship is expressed as the pressure and release (PAR) model, based on the commonly used equation presented in Information Box 1.1. This model enables us to make a number of fairly rudimentary observations about (tectonic) hazards and disasters.

First, if risk (R) is increasing – as reflected, for example, in increased frequency or magnitude of disaster losses (see Figure 1.3) – then hazard (H) and/or vulnerability (V) must be increasing. While there is considerable evidence to show that parts of the world, including possibly the UK, are becoming more exposed to hydrological and meteorological hazards than in the recent past due

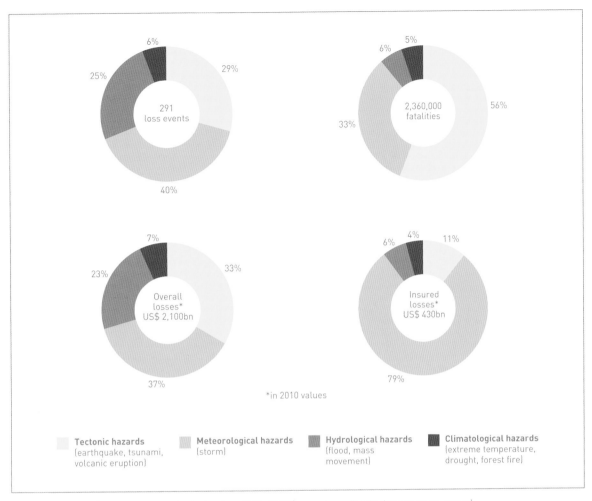

Figure 1.2 Losses from great natural catastrophes, 1950–2010 (percentage distribution per event, group).
Source: The Munich Reinsurance Company.

to the effects of human-accentuated climate change, there is no evidence to show that there have been worldwide increases in levels of seismic and volcanic activity. Hence, if the world is experiencing more tectonic disasters, the primary driver for this must be increased human vulnerability (V) to tectonic hazards.

Second, the PAR model helps us to appreciate the importance of V in creating the massive variability that we see in the forms of natural disasters on Earth. The physical processes that make H are fairly constant between any two comparable tectonic environments around the world, and certainly irrespective of human constructs like political and administrative boundaries within and between countries and regions. So the differences that we see in the types of losses caused by hazards of comparable magnitude in different countries must reflect differences in the construction of vulnerability (human and economic) in different socio-economic and political settings. This can result in an earthquake in one country killing tens of thousands of people and causing millions of dollars of damage, while a very similar physical event in another country kills tens or hundreds people but causes billions of dollars of damage. The same variability occurs at the micro level between different social groupings within a city affected by a single hazard impact.

Finally, it is important to recognise that hazard and vulnerability are interlinked, in that vulnerability can change with the severity and type of hazard. For example, houses may be constructed to resist earthquakes of a particular severity, but will be vulnerable if the intensity of shaking exceeds that. The same structures may be susceptible to even the most minor levels of flooding or windstorm activity.

An additional tier of sophistication can be added to the PAR model by factoring exposure into disaster risk evaluations, so that the risk is a function of hazard, vulnerability and exposure. In essence this approach separates out the internal dimensions of

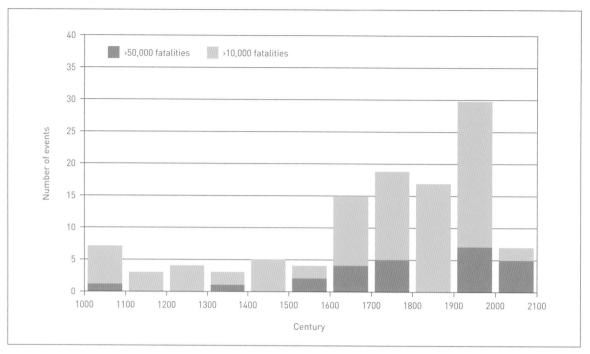

Figure 1.3 Number of earthquakes killing more than 10,000 and 50,000 people per century. **Source:** amended from Jackson, 2006. **Note:** although we are only 11 years into the present century, we have already had the earthquake catastrophes of Gujarat (2001; 20,000 dead), Bam (2003; 30,000 dead), Pakistan (2005; 73,000 dead), Sichuan (2008; 87,000 dead) and Haiti (2010: 220,000 dead), plus the earthquake and tsunami catastrophes of the Indian Ocean (2004; 230,000 dead) and the east coast of Japan (2011; 28,000 dead).

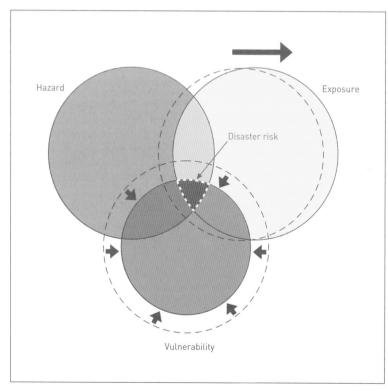

Figure 1.4 The pressure and release model (PAR) of disaster risk. **Source:** Birkmann, 2006. Reproduced with permission of United Nations University Press.

vulnerability, such as financial insecurity and immobility, from external factors, such as location, which are bracketed together as exposure. This is represented diagrammatically in Figure 1.4. The figure is extremely useful in reminding us that, for a given level of hazard, the risk of natural disaster can be reduced by reducing exposure (e.g. through re-location), and/or by reducing vulnerability through mitigation and preparedness actions (Birkmann, 2006).

Global hazard and risk mapping

The UN International Decade for Natural Disaster Reduction (IDNDR), which ran from 1990 to 2000, and the UN International Strategy for Disaster Reduction (ISDR, 2005–15) have spawned a number of efforts to map and characterise global hazard and risk. The World Map of Natural Hazards (Figure 1.5) produced by the Munich Reinsurance Company

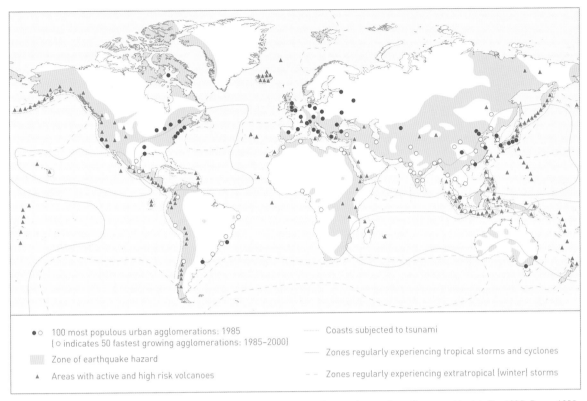

Figure 1.5 The World Map of Natural Hazards and the world's largest urban agglomerations. **Sources:** Munich Re, 1988; Degg, 1992.

● ○ 100 most populous urban agglomerations: 1985
     (○ indicates 50 fastest growing agglomerations: 1985–2000)

▨ Zone of earthquake hazard

▲ Areas with active and high risk volcanoes

.... Coasts subjected to tsunami

—— Zones regularly experiencing tropical storms and cyclones

– – Zones regularly experiencing extratropical (winter) storms

was one of the earliest maps to become widely disseminated, with more specialist hazard mapping projects, including the Global Seismic Hazard Assessment Program (GSHAP) (*www.seismo. ethz.ch/gshap*), 1992–99, following soon after. Between 2004 and 2005 several international indexes of disaster risk management were published, including the Disaster Risk Index (DRI) conceived by United Nations Development Programme (UNDP).

The DRI took more than three years to develop, and was aimed at producing a quantitative index that allows direct comparison of relative risk between countries for disaster management purposes. The first task was to model the frequency and severity of different hazards for different parts of the world (e.g. using data such as that collected for GSHAP). This was then merged with models for population distribution to compute physical exposure. The DRI then used the recent

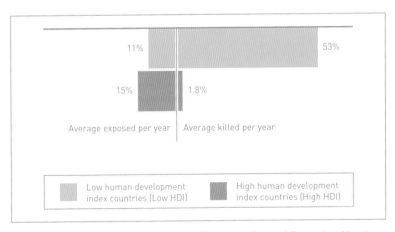

Figure 1.6 Comparing exposure and mortality rates in the world's most and least-developed countries as proportions of total annual global hazard exposure and death toll due to hazard impact. **Source:** Reproduced with kind permission from Springer Science & Business Media: *Natural Hazards*, 'Mapping disastrous natural hazards using global datasets', 35, 2005, Peduzzi, P., Herold, C. and Dao, H.

disaster experiences of countries to calculate the relative vulnerability of each country to principal hazards by dividing the number of people killed by the hazard over a given time period by the number exposed – obviously, the more people killed in proportion to those exposed, the

higher the inferred vulnerability to the hazard.

The results of the DRI are interesting at a range of levels. At the global scale they served to show that although the least developed countries represented 11% of the exposure to hazard, they

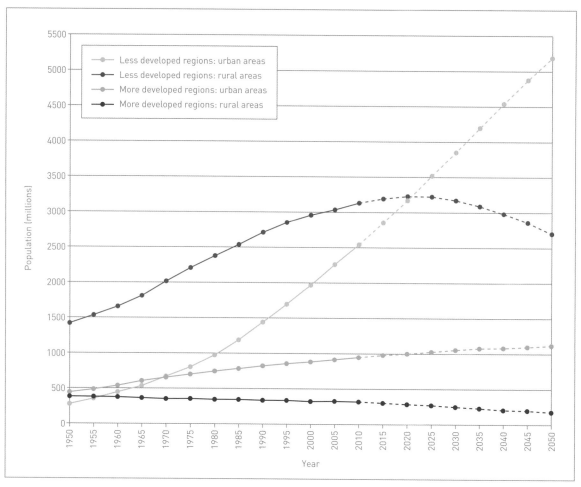

Figure 1.7 Urban and rural population growth, and projections of the developed and developing world. **Source:** United Nations, 2009.

accounted for 53% of the casualties experienced (Figure 1.6). In terms of earthquake hazard specifically, 130 million people worldwide were recorded as being exposed to earthquake risk, with the largest absolute numbers of people being exposed in Japan (30 million), and in Indonesia and the Philippines (16 million each), followed by Taiwan, USA, Chile, Mexico and so on. The most vulnerable states, however, are small island states of the Pacific Rim like Vanuatu and Guam, where every single inhabitant of the country experiences earthquakes on a regular basis.

Urbanisation as an agent of disaster and the global risk transition

The DRI also demonstrated a close relationship between urban growth and the risk of death from tectonic hazards, in particular earthquakes. In the history of the development of human societies over the last 10,000 years, the switch from nomadic (hunter–gatherer) to sedentary ways of life went hand in hand with a changed relationship between people and nature and, in particular, with increased exposure to a range of hazard types. Our nomadic ancestors would simply have uprooted and relocated in the face of a hazardous threat such as rising water levels from a river, or gas and ash emissions from a nearby (volcanic) mountain. Their dwellings would have been lightweight and portable, so that even the strongest of earthquake tremors posed minimal threat. Once societies started to settle, this flexibility of response was lost, and the buildings

that people erected around them gradually became more substantial and thereby life threatening in the event of earthquake-induced structural failure (Jackson, 2006).

Beyond the risks of building failure due to hazard impact, urbanisation has been linked to disaster risk escalation for a number of other less obvious reasons (see Information Box 1.2). Figure 1.7 shows that the focus of world urbanisation switched from the north (developed countries) to the south (developing countries) during the 1970s, heralding a dramatic rise in the risk posed by tectonic hazards to the people and economies of many developing countries (Bilham, 1998). This risk is compounded by the fact that, taken as a whole, the largest cities of the developing world are more

INFORMATION BOX 1.2 URBANISATION AS AN AGENT OF DISASTER

Urbanisation can serve to increase vulnerability to tectonic hazards in a number of ways (Mitchell, 1999; Pelling, 2003). Foremost among these are:

1 The urbanisation process has a concentrating effect upon populations, replacing dispersed rural populations with cities that are foci for population, industry and associated regional and national support structures and institutions (e.g. educational facilities, hospitals, transport infrastructure). This (over-) concentration of people and value increases susceptibility to catastrophic loss if a major population centre experiences a direct strike from a hazardous event. The problem is particularly acute in some developing countries where urban primacy has led to one or two cities dominating their respective countries. For example, 40% of the urban population and 70% of all industry in Peru is situated in and around the capital, Lima, which generates 50% of Peruvian GDP. In comparison London accommodates 12% of the UK population and generates 15% of its GDP.

2 The dramatic rates of growth witnessed by many cities, particularly in developing countries, during the last 40 years have led to acute conditions of overcrowding that compound vulnerability to hazard. Overcrowding makes safe evacuation more difficult, and tends to result in more and more people being housed in poor housing conditions. Pressure on space in and around overcrowded cities can encourage development of marginal areas (i.e. those that are more exposed to hazards) avoided by populations in the past,

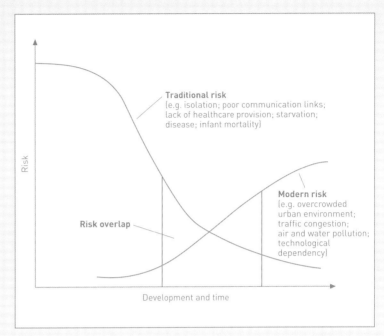

Figure 1.8 The environmental risk transition. Note that the total risk (traditional plus modern) declines with time through the development process. **Source:** Kasperson and Kasperson (2001).

such as unstable slopes (e.g. around Bogotá or Rio de Janeiro) or low-lying areas susceptible to tsunami inundation.

3 Urbanisation typically goes hand in hand with the development of relatively complex and sophisticated transport and utility networks (e.g. for power distribution, communications). This increases the susceptibility to disruption caused by relatively minor as well as major hazard impacts.

4 People in cities tend to be less self-reliant than rural dwellers in preparing for, and responding to, hazard impacts. They are more likely to expect civic authorities to take centralised (top-down) actions to protect them from hazards, and less likely to feel a need to protect themselves. They are also more likely to feel that the physical presence of the city around them affords a degree of

protection from hazard. This lack of individual and community awareness and preparedness can increase vulnerability, particularly if the capacity of authorities to deliver an effective hazard response becomes compromised.

5 Differential ageing and uneven replacement of buildings and infrastructure within large cities produces a patchwork of vulnerability than can be very complex to manage (Mitchell, 1999).

Collectively these factors might be grouped under the notion of risk transition (see Figure 1.8). Traditional risks in rural areas, such as isolation and distance from health care following a disaster impact, are being replaced by modern risks associated with congested urban environments and lack of individual and community self-reliance (Kasperson and Kasperson, 2001).

exposed to tectonic hazards than their counterparts in the north (e.g. see Figures 1.5 and 6.1). The rates of urbanisation in the south during the last four decades have also far outstripped anything seen in the north (where the growth of large cities was generally a gradual process spanning a number of centuries), compounding the pressures described in Information Box 1.2. In 1950 just five of the world's 15 largest cities were in the south; by 2015, only three (Tokyo, New York and Los Angeles) will be in the north. Today 22 cities and urban regions have been designated 'megacities' by the UN because they have populations exceeding 10 million people, but only six of them are in the north. It is sobering to think of the concentrations of people and value in such areas, and to consider that 18 (→80%) of them are exposed to tectonic (primarily earthquake) hazards, seven of them at a high level and a further six at medium level (Munich Re, 2004).

Hazard perception and response
In order to respond to a risky situation, people need to be aware of, or perceive, that situation and have the option to take action if they are uncomfortable with it. Hazard perception and response is a fascinating area of study in its own right, and one that is important to disaster mitigation at all levels within society. Individual perception of surroundings is influenced by a wide range of factors, including age, education, gender, personality and, of particular importance to the perception of natural hazards, experience of previous hazard impacts: the more severe the experience, generally the greater the awareness of hazard and risk (Park, 1991; Smith and Petley, 2009). These influences serve to ensure that, within any one group of people, there is considerable variation in how people perceive and respond to risk, adding complexity and uncertainty to

INFORMATION BOX 1.3
KEY PARADIGMS OF DISASTER

A paradigm is a way of viewing things. There are two very influential paradigms in the study of natural disasters.

The **dominant paradigm** (also referred to as the environmentally deterministic or behavioural paradigm) emphasises the importance of informed choice to disaster mitigation, and the capacity for engineering and scientific interventions (i.e. environmental or technical fixes) to overcome environmental constraints. This top-down, resource-intensive approach to visualising disaster dominated (Western) government and inter-governmental efforts to manage hazard and risk in the 20th century, with an emphasis on physical hazard monitoring/prediction/control measures coupled with emergency planning, land use regulation and public training programmes.

The **alternative paradigm** (also referred to as the socially deterministic or structural paradigm) emerged in the 1970s as a critique of the above, in that it views disasters as inevitable consequences of deep-rooted and long-standing socio-economic and political processes and pressures that create conditions of vulnerability and constrain individual choice (e.g. slum settlements develop on unstable slopes out of a lack of alternatives rather than a lack of awareness). Hazard events are viewed merely as trigger mechanisms for disasters that are waiting to happen. The approach advocates community-based (bottom-up) mitigation strategies that reduce vulnerability to hazard at the local level as part of a wider poverty alleviation and development agenda, coupled with fundamental political, social and economic reform at regional and national levels to redistribute wealth and power.

disaster management.

Views on the importance of perception to disaster management have varied, particularly in the context of international development. This is reflected in two contrasting schools of thought (paradigms) that have been very influential in efforts to understand disasters and manage their impact (see Information Box 1.3). In the dominant (or behavioural) paradigm, natural disasters are seen primarily as consequences of environmental processes, compounded by inappropriate human actions in the face of such threats due to perceived ignorance/

lack of awareness. The alternative (or structural) paradigm argues that such actions, particularly in poor communities, frequently arise out of lack of choice rather than lack of awareness, and prefers to view disasters as consequences of socio-political processes that constrain people and make them vulnerable (Chester, 1993; Smith and Petley, 2009). As we shall see in Chapter 6, the current International Strategy for Disaster Reduction (ISDR) prefers to place emphasis on building resilience to hazards at the individual and community level, and increased hazard awareness must be part and parcel of this.

Scope of this book

In this book we seek to enliven the perspectives and theoretical concepts outlined in this chapter using the three principal tectonic hazards of earthquake, volcano and tsunami. This task is made all the easier by the large number of recent examples of major hazard impact that we can draw upon, each a testament to humanity's continuing vulnerability to these hazards, almost irrespective of the large amount that we already know about the physical and social processes that shape tectonic disasters. The starting point has to be a consideration of the physical basis of such disasters – tectonic processes. We then consider each of the three principal hazard types, exploring hazard, vulnerability and response in equal measure. The concluding chapter summarises the principal challenges for the current generation of disaster managers, and flags up key things to look out for in the years ahead.

ACTIVITY BOX 1

1   Apply the vulnerability progression model to a named tectonic hazard event such as the 2010 Haiti earthquake. Make a blank copy of the framework and replace it with researched detail.
2   Research the CRED disaster base at *www.emdat.be/ natural-disasters-trends* to examine the idea that there is an upward trend in both social and economic losses from tectonic hazards.
3   Research earthquakes of 6+ magnitude that have occurred since 1985. Draw a graph or carry out research to relate magnitude to the number of deaths. Explore at least two anomalies, one positive and one negative.

References

Bilham, R. (1998) 'Earthquakes and urban development', *Nature*, pp. 625–6.

Birkmann, J. (ed) (2006) *Measuring Vulnerability to Natural Hazards: Towards disaster resilient societies*. Tokyo: UNU Press.

Blaikie, P., Cannon, T., Davis, I. and Wisner, B. (1994; 2004) *At Risk: Natural hazards, people's vulnerability and disaster* (1st/2nd editions). Abingdon: Routledge.

Chester, D. (1993) *Volcanoes and Society*. London: Arnold.

Degg, M.R. (1992) 'Natural disasters: recent trends and future prospects', *Geography*, 77, 3, pp. 198–209.

Jackson, J. (2006) 'Fatal attraction: living with earthquakes, the growth of villages into megacities, and earthquake vulnerability in the modern world', *Philosophical Transactions of the Royal Society A*, 364, pp. 1911–25.

Kasperson, J.X. and Kasperson, R.E. (eds) (2001) *Global Environmental Risk*. London: Earthscan.

Mitchell, J.K. (ed) (1999) *Crucibles of Hazard: Mega-cities and disasters in transition*. Tokyo: UNU.

Munich Re (1988) *World Map of Natural Hazards*. Munich: The Munich Reinsurance Company.

Munich Re (1999) *Topics 2000: Natural Catastrophes – The Current Position*. Munich: The Munich Reinsurance Company.

Munich Re (2004) *Megacities – Megarisks: Trends and challenges for insurance and risk management*. Munich: The Munich Reinsurance Company.

Park, C.C. (1991) *Environmental Hazards* (2nd edition). Basingstoke: Macmillan.

Peduzzi, P., Herold, C. and Dao, H. (2005) 'Mapping disastrous natural hazards using global datasets', *Natural Hazards*, 35, 2, pp. 265–89.

Pelling, M. (2003) *The Vulnerability of Cities: Natural disasters and social resilience*. London: Earthscan.

Smith, K. and Petley, D. (2009) *Environmental Hazards: Assessing risk and reducing disaster*. Abingdon: Routledge.

United Nations (2009) *World Urbanization Prospects: The 2009 Revision*. New York: United Nations Department of Economic and Social Affairs.

 Extra resources to accompany this chapter are available on the Top Spec web pages. See page 4 for further information.

2. Tectonic processes

Earth's tectonic plates

The modern theory of plate tectonics recognises seven large tectonic plates plus a further seven smaller plates. There are also dozens of microplates. Tectonic plates are made of two types of crust: oceanic and continental (Figure 2.1). Some plates, such as the Nazca plate, consist of wholly oceanic crust, whereas others, such as the African plate, consist of both continental and oceanic crust.

Continental crust has formed slowly over billions of years, most likely at subduction zones. The low-density, granitic material of continental crust is not capable of being subducted, which helps explain its great age. Oceanic crust is formed continually at constructive plate margins, but this high-density material is destroyed at subduction zones and thus is limited in age to a few hundred million years.

Wegener's revolutionary ideas

The idea that the Earth's tectonic plates are in constant motion is widely known and accepted today, yet when this idea was first proposed by Alfred Wegener just over 100 years ago, it was almost universally dismissed. Wegener was a German meteorologist, not a geologist, so when he published *The Origins of Continents and Oceans* in 1915, it was seen as the work of a scientific outsider and described as 'utter, damned rot' by W.B. Scott,

then president of the influential American Philosophical Society.

Wegener's theory, continental drift, proposed that continents had once been joined together and had subsequently 'drifted' apart. Today, evidence from fossils and geological formations proves this theory to be correct, but this evidence was not accepted in the early 20th century. Continental drift theory could provide no mechanism that might explain how continents move and because of this the theory was incomplete. It would take decades of further research before Wegener's ideas were accepted (Figure 2.2), although by the late 1960s many key breakthroughs had led to the widespread adoption of plate tectonics as the new geological paradigm.

Plate motion

For plate tectonics to work, there needs to be some mechanism to move the plates. Proving what this mechanism is presents scientists with a problem due to the inaccessible nature of the Earth's interior. Seismic waves generated by earthquakes have been used to probe the interior, rather like X-rays are used to investigate the human body. Shear waves (S-waves) and compressional waves (P-waves) travelling through the Earth speed up and slow down as they transverse different layers within the Earth's interior.

Figure 2.3 shows the changing velocity of a P-wave from the surface to the Earth's centre. P-waves travel fastest through dense solids. Figure 2.3 shows that density generally increases with depth as does P-wave velocity. There are two exceptions:

- P-wave velocity drops dramatically at around 3000km depth. This is because P-waves are passing from the solid mantle to the liquid outer core. Density increases because the core is metallic (iron/nickel) whereas the mantle is rocky.
- P-wave velocity drops at a depth of 100–300km in a region known as the low-velocity zone (LVZ). The drop may be because some liquid is present at this depth.

A reasonable explanation of the LVZ is that here the upper mantle is partly molten (perhaps 5% molten by volume) and that the layer

INFORMATION BOX 2.1
THE EARTH'S CRUST

The outermost layer of the solid earth is called the lithosphere (the 'rocky sphere'). The uppermost layer of the lithosphere is the crust. This layer is brittle and cool, reaching temperatures of around 200°C at the boundary between the crust and lithospheric mantle below. The crustal part of the lithosphere ranges in thickness from 5km to 75km, with the lithospheric mantle extending down a further 50–100km. The lithosphere is broken up into numerous tectonic or lithospheric plates, both oceanic and continental in composition.

	Oceanic	Continental
Maximum age	180 million years	3.5 billion years
Thickness (km)	6–10	25–75
Area of Earth's surface	60%	40%
Density (grams/cm³)	3.3	2.7
Rock type	Basaltic	Granitic

Figure 2.1 Comparing oceanic and continental crust.

1927	Arthur Holmes suggests that radioactive decay in the Earth's core could generate enough heat to create convection currents in the Earth's mantle.
1940s	Hugo Benioff uses the foci of earthquakes to plot the form of descending slabs of oceanic plates at subduction zones.
Early 1960s	Harry Hess, Fred Vine and Drummond Matthews show that new oceanic crust forms at constructive plate margins through the process of sea floor spreading. J. Tuzo Wilson shows that tectonic plates move over stationary hot spots.
1990s	Satellites utilise laser and GPS measurement to accurately measure and track plate movements as small as a few millimetres.

Figure 2.2 From continental drift to plate tectonics.

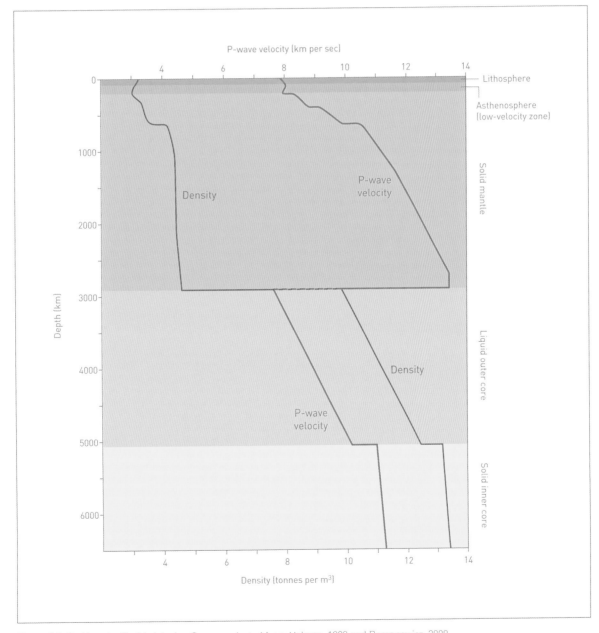

Figure 2.3 Probing the Earth's interior. **Source:** adapted from Holmes, 1993 and Romanowicz, 2008.

immediately beneath the lithosphere is therefore a weak, plastic and deformable layer which behaves like a very viscous fluid. This layer is often called the asthenosphere. Rigid lithospheric plates appear to be able to move because of the 'lubricating' asthenosphere below.

Drag, pull or push?

The engine of plate tectonics is the heat generated by radioactive decay within the Earth. Radioactive isotopes such as Potassium 40, Uranium 238 and Thorium 232 produce heat, which rises through the mantle, in plumes, towards the crust. These plumes form the rising limbs of huge convection cells within the mantle. Where these plumes meet the base of the lithosphere, they diverge and the lithosphere is pulled apart forming a constructive plate margin. The forces acting on moving plates are complex (Figure 2.4) and it is not clear which forces are the most important.

The force exerted by a cold, dense oceanic plate sinking at a subduction zone may be important. In the Atlantic Ocean, where there are few subduction zones, plate motion is around 10–15mm per year. In the Pacific Ocean, which is surrounded by subduction zones forming the Ring of Fire, plates move at 60–80mm per year.

Plate margins

The boundaries, or margins, where plates meet are the location for the majority of volcanic and seismic activity. The range of plate margin types is outlined in Figure 2.5. Volcanic activity which is found far from a plate margin is associated with hot spots. A hot spot occurs when an isolated column of hot mantle material (known as a mantle plume) rises beneath either an oceanic plate (e.g. at Hawaii or the Galapagos Islands) or a continental plate (e.g. Yellowstone in the USA). Rising magma breaks through the overlying plate and erupts, often forming a chain of volcanoes, both

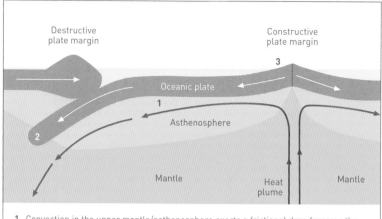

1 Convection in the upper mantle/asthenosphere exerts a frictional drag force on the plate, pulling it along.

2 The weight of the cold, dense sinking slab of oceanic plate pulls the plate downward (slab-pull force). There may also be a suctional force pulling the subducting plate downward.

3 Upwelling, hot mantle material causes mid-ocean ridges to be topographically higher than the surrounding ocean plate; the force of gravity pulls the plate from the high ridge towards the subducting end of the plate.

Figure 2.4 The forces of plate motion.

active and extinct, if the overlying plate continues to move over the hot spot. Earthquakes can occur in intraplate locations (mid-plate) as well as at plate margins. The 2001 Gujarat earthquake in India, which killed 20,000 people, occurred a long way from any plate margin. Intraplate earthquakes result from reactivation of existing faults, probably as a result of a long-term build-up of strain within the plate. The causes of intraplate earthquakes are poorly understood. Transference of stress from plate boundaries to plate interiors is a possible mechanism, but further research is needed.

Some plate margins involve more than two plates. These are complex 'triple' junctions where three plates meet. Some are relatively simple, if highly unstable, such as the triple subduction zone trench system off the east coast of Japan. Triple junctions can involve both constructive and destructive margins. This is the case where the Juan de Fuca Ridge, a constructive margin splitting the Pacific and Juan de Fuca plates, intersects the North American Plate and the Cascadia subduction zone.

Tectonic landscapes ancient and modern

Tectonic processes generate landscapes that contain a suite of typical landforms. When active tectonic processes end, these landforms are modified, or softened, by weathering and erosion processes. Figure 2.6 shows Sunset Crater, a volcanic cinder cone which formed around AD1000–1100 as a result of a hot spot beneath the North American plate. In the centuries since eruption, the area has become partly vegetated but is still clearly volcanic in origin.

Tectonic landscapes can be either active or relict. Where plate motion is creating a landscape today it is active. Many tectonic landscapes are now far from an active plate margin and are relict landscapes. Relict landscapes are weathered and eroded evidence of past tectonic activity.

Rift systems occur when tectonic plates pull apart, leading to crustal extension. Active rifts today occur undersea such as the Mid-Atlantic Ridge, or on land as in the African Rift Valley. Rifts are characterised by:

Plate margin type	Examples	Processes	Hazards
Oceanic constructive	Mid-Atlantic Ridge; Carlsberg Ridge (Indian Ocean)	As plates move apart, tension causes rifting at the centre of the ocean ridge. Magma, generated by dry partial melting of the upper mantle, is intruded into the rift zone. Earthquakes are often magmatic in origin.	Effusive, basaltic volcanic eruptions; minor, shallow earthquakes
Continental constructive	African Rift Valley	Tectonic extension causes crustal thinning. The development of normal faults leads to rift formation. Magma can penetrate the thinned, faulted crust.	Effusive, basaltic volcanic eruptions; minor, shallow earthquakes
Oceanic–continental destructive	Peru–Chile Trench and Andean mountain range	Friction between the subducting oceanic plate and the overlying plate leads to an inclined zone of earthquake generation known as a Benioff Zone, which may extend to depths of 600km. Wet partial melting of the subducting plate leads to the formation of andesitic magmas.	Explosive, andesitic eruptions; major earthquakes of variable depth; tsunami
Oceanic–oceanic destructive	Caribbean island arc; Aleutian Islands		
Continental collision zone	Himalayas	Low-density crust crumples under compression, creating fold mountain ranges cut by major fault zones.	Major, shallow earthquakes along thrust faults; volcanic activity very rare
Conservative	San Andreas Fault; North Anatolian Fault	Plates slowly slide past each other, often in a jerky motion punctuated by periods of rising strain as friction prevents motion, leading to infrequent but major earthquakes.	Major, shallow earthquakes; no volcanic activity

Figure 2.5 Plate margins and their tectonic hazards.

- a linear mountain range (ridge), which forms as the buoyancy of hot, low-density magma below forces the crust to bulge upwards along the length of the plate margin
- a central rift within the ridge, formed due to subsidence and collapse between normal faults, bounded by steep scarp slopes
- at continental rifts, central areas frequently occupied by lakes or, as the rift opens, by the sea (as in the Red Sea)
- numerous, albeit relatively small, basaltic volcanic eruptions generating cinder cones, larger volcanoes and lava flows
- minor igneous intrusions such as dykes, common in rifts because, as faulting and rifting occurs, magma rises through the faults and fissures.

In Scotland, the Isle of Arran represents the relict landscape of an ancient rift zone. It was active

Figure 2.6 Sunset Crater volcanic cinder cone and lava flow, Arizona, USA.
Photo: Cameron Dunn.

50–60 million years ago when the Eurasian plate split from the North American plate and the Atlantic Ocean began to open up. Arran's northern mountains are the eroded granitic root of an ancient volcano and the island is cut by igneous intrusions such as dykes and sills.

Throughout geological time, periodic episodes of enhanced volcanic activity have created large igneous provinces (LIPs) (Figure 2.7). Some LIPs, such as India's Deccan Traps, the Siberian Traps and the Columbia River Basalts, are quite famous relict volcanic landscapes. These landscapes consist of hundreds of vast basaltic lava flows stacked one on top of another. Where the flows have eroded or been incised by rivers, the landscape often appears as a series of steps – hence the term 'trap topography' from the Swedish word for stairs (trappa). In Washington State and Oregon, USA, the Columbia River Basalts form a 2km thick pile of basaltic lava flows that erupted over a period of several million years between 17 and 14 million years ago. Today the landscape is one of high plateaux dissected by river gorges whose sides reveal the horizontal lava flows. The Columbia River Basalts

cover an area of over 150,000km^2, whereas the more ancient Siberian Traps extend over 1,500,000km^2.

Examining a world map of active volcanoes, it is easy to see how common island arc systems are. Island arcs are curving chains of volcanic islands. Examples include the Aleutian Islands off Alaska, the Caribbean islands and the Philippine islands. Island arcs are a result of collision between two oceanic plates. Normally the older, colder, marine sediment-laden oceanic plate subducts (descends) beneath younger oceanic crust. Along the plate boundary a deep oceanic trench forms; the Mariana Trench in the Pacific Ocean is in excess of 10km deep. A few hundred kilometres from the trench, in the direction of plate descent, a chain of volcanoes forms. These are composite cone andesitic volcanoes and are often highly explosive such as Krakatoa in Indonesia or Soufrière Hills on Montserrat in the Caribbean.

The tectonic landscape of continental collision zones such as the Himalaya is that of an orogenic (mountain) belt. As continents collide, the crust is compressed. Some crustal material is forced upwards, forming mountains, and

some is forced down into the upper mantle, creating a 'root' which mirrors the mountains above. The Himalaya is a geologically active orogenic belt. Formation began around 70 million years ago due to collision between the northwards-moving Indo-Australian plate and the Eurasian plate. This movement continues today at a rate of around 7cm per year, with the Himalaya rising by around 5mm per year. The mountains themselves are characterised by major folding of the crust and thrust faulting. Steep slopes, subsequently deeply incised by rivers and glaciers, have been additionally weakened by faulting and fracturing, which makes them geologically unstable and prone to landslides.

Some tectonic landscapes are smaller and more subtle than major rift systems, island arc chains and continental collision zones. It is possible to trace major faults at conservative plate margins, such as the San Andreas Fault in California, through the landscape as shown in Figure 2.8.

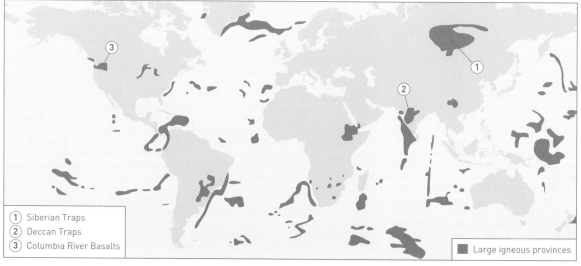

1 Siberian Traps
2 Deccan Traps
3 Columbia River Basalts

■ Large igneous provinces

Figure 2.7 Large igneous provinces (LIPs). **Source:** Short, 1996.

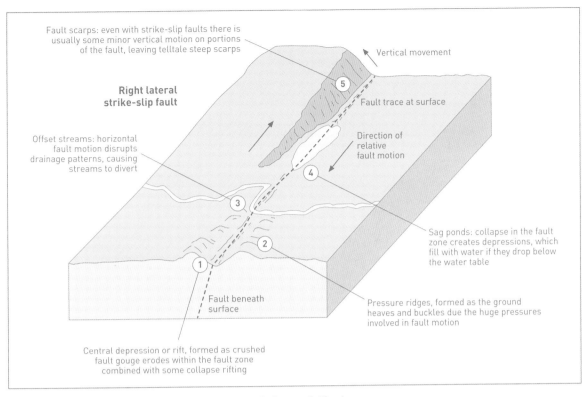

Fault scarps: even with strike-slip faults there is usually some minor vertical motion on portions of the fault, leaving telltale steep scarps

Vertical movement

Right lateral strike-slip fault

Fault trace at surface

Offset streams: horizontal fault motion disrupts drainage patterns, causing streams to divert

Direction of relative fault motion

Sag ponds: collapse in the fault zone creates depressions, which fill with water if they drop below the water table

Fault beneath surface

Pressure ridges, formed as the ground heaves and buckles due the huge pressures involved in fault motion

Central depression or rift, formed as crushed fault gouge erodes within the fault zone combined with some collapse rifting

Figure 2.8 Landscape features of the active San Andreas fault zone, California.
Source: USGS website.

ACTIVITY BOX 2

1 Get hold of some granite and basalt rock samples (most geography, geology and science departments will have these), which represent continental and oceanic crust. Examine them and describe the differences in density, colour and texture/crystal size.

2 Explain the significance of the asthenosphere in plate motion.

3 Use an outline world map to label the major tectonic plates and plate boundaries that make up the Pacific Ring of Fire.

4 Outline the evidence in Figure 2.5 that suggests some types of plate boundary are more hazardous places to live near than others.

5 Describe and explain the landscape features of two contrasting types of plate boundary.

6 There are many good websites that can help you understand the different types of plate boundary/margin. Check out the USGS plate motion website at *http://pubs.usgs.gov/gip/dynamic/understanding.html#anchor15039288* NASA also has a website with animations at *http://scign.jpl.nasa.gov/learn/plate4.htm* There are also some good animations at *www.nature.nps.gov/geology/usgsnps/animate/pltecan.html*

References

Holmes, A. (1993) *Principles of Physical Geology* (4th edition). Cheltenham: Nelson Thornes.

Romanowicz, B. (2008) 'Using seismic waves to image Earth's internal structure', *Nature*, 451, 7176, pp. 266–8.

Short, N.M. (1996) *The Remote Sensing Tutorial*. NASA Goddard Space Flight Center/Global Science and Technology/USAF Academy. Available online at *www.fas.org/irp/imint/docs/rst/Front/overview.html* (last accessed 13 June 2011).

United States Geological Service (USGS) website: *www.usgs.gov* (last accessed 17 November 2011).

 Extra resources to accompany this chapter are available on the Top Spec web pages. See page 4 for further information.

3. Earthquake hazard

Earthquakes remain one of the most feared natural hazards because of their ability to strike completely without warning, causing death and destruction in a matter of seconds, and creating conditions of chaos and disorder that can take even the most affluent of societies decades to recover from. This continuing threat is in some ways at odds with our understanding of earthquake hazard, because we know so much about the parameters that influence earthquake hazard generally, and the geography of earthquake hazard in particular – e.g. where earthquakes are most likely to occur, the likely size of future events, which areas locally will experience the worst shaking and what types of structure will be most susceptible (vulnerable) to that shaking. But what we are unable to say, with any real certainty at present, is exactly *when* that shaking will occur – and therein lies the unpredictability and fear factor of the earthquake as a hazard.

Current understanding of earthquake science demands that societies and individuals take a longer-term perspective in hazard mitigation, by planning for events that we know are going to occur sooner or later, but which may well not occur in the near future. The horrific death tolls that continue to be recorded from earthquake impacts in rich and poor countries around the world (Figure 3.1) testify to people's inability, for a wide range of reasons, to respond effectively in this manner. Human beings tend to think and operate on short timescales (e.g. the five-year term of an elected government in a rich Western society, or the day-to-day, hand-to-mouth existence of a slum dweller in a poor one). Earthquakes operate on a different (geological) timescale that human societies, generally speaking, are poorly adjusted to deal with.

Earthquake distribution, size and frequency

At a global level the relationship between the distribution of seismic activity and plate tectonics is well established. The two principal belts of global seismic activity are the Alpine–Himalayan collision zone and the circum-Pacific 'Ring of Fire'. The former accounts for about 23% of annual global seismic energy release, and is mainly associated with collision between continental plates, generating fold mountain tectonic landscapes and relatively shallow earthquakes – i.e. those in which the focus or point of origin of the earthquake within the crust is less than 60km below the surface. The circum-Pacific belt accounts for the majority (over 75%) of earthquake activity on the Earth, most of this linked to the subduction of sections of oceanic plate beneath the continental margins of the Pacific rim. The subduction process generates earthquakes of a range of focal depths, and the volcanic and tsunami hazards that characterise many parts of this seismic region (see Figure 2.5).

Figure 3.1 includes earthquake disasters from both these seismic belts. In terms of relative size, the earthquakes can be compared most directly using the earthquake magnitude (M) scale, which provides a calibrated measure of the amount of energy released in an earthquake event. The scale was originally developed in the 1930s for use in southern California by the US seismologist Charles Richter, but has been adapted a number of times since then. The version in common use today is the moment magnitude scale, based on a number of parameters

Date	Region	Magnitude	Fatalities
11 March 2011	East Coast of Honshu, Japan	9.0	28,050 *
12 January 2010	Port au Prince, Haiti	7.0	220,000
30 September 2009	Southern Sumatra, Indonesia	7.5	1,117
12 May 2008	Eastern Sichuan, China	7.9	87,587
26 May 2006	Java, Indonesia	6.3	5,749
8 October 2005	Kashmir, NE Pakistan/NW India	7.6	73,000
26 December 2004	Northern Sumatra and Indian Ocean	9.1	227,898 *
26 December 2003	Bam, SE Iran	6.6	30,000
25 March 2002	Hindu Kush, Afghanistan	6.1	1,000
21 January 2001	Gujarat, NW India	7.9	20,023
17 August 1999	Izmit (Kocaeli), Western Turkey	7.6	17,225
30 May 1998	Afghanistan/Tajikistan border	6.6	4,000
10 May 1997	Northern Iran	7.3	1,572
16 January 1995	Kobe, Japan	6.9	5,530
29 September 1993	Latur, Central India	6.2	9,748

* includes fatalities due to tsunami impact

Figure 3.1 The deadliest earthquakes of the last 20 years. **Source:** USGS Earthquake Hazards Program website.

of an earthquake event, including the area of fault rupture and the amount of fault movement involved. The earthquakes in Figure 3.1 made the headlines because they impacted on populated areas, but thousands of other medium–strong events occurred during the same time period and went unnoticed or unreported by the international media. Figure 3.2 shows the approximate annual frequency of earthquakes in different magnitude bands, and the descriptive terms applied to these. It is important to remember that the earthquake magnitude scale is a logarithmic scale, not a linear one, so that a unit increase in magnitude involves a 10-fold increase in the amount of ground motion and a 32-fold increase in the amount of energy released (Keller and Blodgett, 2008). It takes 32 M=8.0 earthquakes – comparable to that which killed 20,000 people in Gujarat, India, in 2001 – to release the same amount of energy as one M=9.0 earthquake like that in Japan in 2011!

Figure 3.1 also reminds us that there is not necessarily a direct relationship between earthquake magnitude and the size of the earthquake impact. The circum-Pacific region has experienced a number of truly great seismic events in recent years associated with mega-thrust ruptures of extensive sections (→400km) of subduction plate boundary. In comparison, the largest earthquakes of the Alpine–Himalayan belt have tended to be in the strong to major magnitude categories, yet their impact in human terms has often been just as great as that caused by larger events along the Pacific rim due to local site effects and conditions of vulnerability within the human settlements affected. Occasionally moderate to strong earthquakes occur in intraplate areas far removed from the plate boundaries, due to the presence of ancient structural weaknesses within the crust or volcanic hot spots. They can be particularly devastating

Descriptor	Magnitude	Average annual number of events
Great	8 and higher	1
Major	7–7.9	17
Strong	6–6.9	134
Moderate	5–5.9	1319
Light	4–4.9	13,000 (estimated)
Minor	3–3.9	130,000 (estimated)
Very minor	2–2.9	1,300,000 (estimated) (approx. 150 per hour)

Figure 3.2 Earthquake magnitude (M) descriptors and annual frequency. **Source:** USGS.

because they are often totally unexpected and so impact on communities that are very poorly prepared for such eventualities – for example, the Liège earthquake in Belgium in 1983, which damaged 16,000 houses despite its relatively small size (M=4.7), and the 1993 Killari or Latur earthquake (M=6.3) in central India, which killed around 20,000 people. Some of the most damaging earthquakes to hit North America in the last 200 years were centred not around the San Andreas Fault in California, but around New Madrid (Missouri) and Charleston (South Carolina) in the eastern US.

Earthquake ground motions and site effects

Earthquakes are essentially shock waves radiating out from a fault rupture (the focus) like ripples from a stone thrown into a pond. The waves travel through the Earth (body waves) and across its surface (surface waves). There are two types of body wave: compressional or primary (P) waves and shear or secondary (S) waves. The primary waves travel fastest through the crust and so are the first to be sensed after an earthquake has occurred. As the body waves reach the point on the Earth's surface directly above the focus (i.e. the epicentre) they generate an array of surface waves that radiate out as a mixture of horizontal (Love waves) and vertical ground motions. These waves travel more slowly than the body waves and are responsible for most of the damage experienced in

earthquakes (Bryant, 2005; Keller and Blodgett, 2008).

Variations in the surface effects of shock waves, and in the severity of shaking they cause, are often attributable to differences in the way surface materials transmit seismic energy. The effects of earthquake shaking on the surface, and on buildings and humans, are often summarised using earthquake intensity (I) scales, such as that presented in Figure 3.3. These scales are descriptive and therefore provide a more qualitative and subjective assessment of the size of an earthquake than the magnitude scales discussed above, but they are extremely useful for indentifying local conditions that increase or reduce the severity of shaking experienced in an earthquake. Following the great San Francisco earthquake of 1906, geologists were able to use such scales to show that the shaking was far more intense in low-lying districts of the city situated on soft sediment and artificially reclaimed land (fill) surrounding San Francisco Bay, and that areas beyond the bay with solid rock underpinnings experienced less severe shaking, even though many were closer to the earthquake epicentre (Zeilinga de Boer and Sanders, 2005). This same relationship has been demonstrated in countless subsequent earthquakes, including those in Managua (1972), Mexico City (1985) and Loma Prieta (California) (1989) (see Figure 3.4).

Intensity	Effects
I	Felt by very few people under especially favourable conditions.
II	Felt by only a few persons at rest, especially on upper floors of buildings.
III	Felt quite noticeably indoors, especially on upper floors of buildings. Many people do not recognise it as an earthquake. Standing vehicles may rock slightly. Vibration feels like the passing of a truck.
IV	During the day, felt indoors by many, outdoors by few. At night some awakened. Dishes, windows, doors disturbed. Walls make a cracking sound. Sensation like a heavy truck striking the building. Standing vehicles rock noticeably.
V	Felt by nearly everyone; many awakened. Some dishes and windows broken. Unstable objects overturned.
VI	Felt by all; many frightened. Some heavy furniture moved. A few instances of fallen plaster or damaged chimneys. Damage slight.
VII	Damage negligible in buildings of good design and construction; slight to moderate in well-built ordinary structures; considerable in poorly built or badly designed structures; some chimneys broken. Noticed by vehicle drivers.
VIII	Damage slight in specially designed structures; considerable damage in ordinary substantial buildings with partial collapse; damage great in poorly built structures; fall of chimneys, factory stacks, columns, monuments and walls. Heavy furniture overturned. Disturbs vehicle drivers.
IX	Damage considerable in specially designed structures; well-designed frame structures thrown out of plumb. Damage great in substantial buildings, with partial collapse. Buildings shifted off foundations. Underground pipes broken.
X	Some well-built wooden structures are destroyed; most masonry and frame structures with foundations destroyed; train rails bent.
XI	Few if any masonry structures remain standing. Bridges destroyed. Underground pipelines taken out of service. Train rails bent greatly.
XII	Damage total. Waves seen on ground surfaces. Lines of sight and level are distorted. Objects thrown up in the air.

Figure 3.3 Earthquake intensity (I) scale. Note the use of Roman numerals to distinguish intensity values from earthquake magnitude (M) measurements (Figure 3.2). **Source:** USGS.

Soft, unconsolidated sediments slow down the passage of earthquake shock waves, and in so doing can amplify and prolong the severity of shaking. The strength of this effect can vary with the distance from an earthquake epicentre because the nature of the seismic ground motions changes as they radiate away from the source. Earthquakes generate both high-frequency/short period (many cycles per second) and low-frequency/long period wave motions, with the former attenuating (fading out) more quickly than the latter as the energy moves away from the epicentral area, to leave motions of predominantly low frequencies of vibration at larger epicentral distances (see Figure 3.5). It is these slower rhythmic motions that are most likely to be amplified by soft sediments, as demonstrated to catastrophic effect in the Mexico City earthquake of 1985, in which massive devastation was caused to a relatively small part of this huge city, despite the fact that it was situated over 350km from the earthquake epicentre off the Pacific coast. Damage was concentrated in buildings of 5–15 storeys around the old core of the city situated on a drained lake bed underlain by highly compressible sediment. Elsewhere in the city, many residents living and working in districts situated on solid rock went about their daily business, completely unaware that a distant earthquake had inflicted massive death and destruction on parts of the downtown area of their city just a few kilometres away.

Other localised ground effects include earthquake-triggered landsliding and soil liquefaction. The former is most acute in areas of steep terrain, and has been a major contributing factor to the severity and extent of earthquake impact in the uplifted and steeply incised landscapes of the Alpine–Himalayan continental collision zone. For example, the Kashmir (northern Pakistan and NW India) earthquake of 2005 triggered thousands of landslides, which devastated villages and roads, isolating communities for weeks and months following the event, and severely hampering the emergency relief and recovery processes.

Liquefaction is a process through which water-saturated sediment loses its cohesion during violent earthquake shaking, causing the sediment to collapse and lose bearing strength. Porewater is forced out onto the surface in geyser-like emissions to create mud/sand 'volcanoes' and deposit sheets of sediment (see Figure 3.6), and buildings and structures situated on the liquefied sediment may sink or topple (Murck *et al.*, 1997). In contrast to earthquake-triggered landsliding, liquefaction is typically associated with areas of poorly drained flat land adjacent to rivers and coasts – areas that also tend to be attractive for human habitation.

Earthquakes and buildings

Earthquake vulnerability is largely about buildings: about 75% of earthquake fatalities are caused by building collapse (Coburn and Spence, 2002). People die or lose their livelihoods in earthquakes because the buildings that they erect to live in and work in fail to resist earthquake motions. In this respect the earthquake hazard is a hazard largely of our own making. It dates from a point in the evolution of human civilisation when people started to adopt sedentary ways of life and build permanent structures in which to live (see Chapter 1).

Much of the damage and structural failure that buildings experience in earthquakes is caused by horizontal or shearing (sideways) motions. Ask any child to build a house from dominoes and he/she will tend to put up something that, to a lesser or greater extent, resists the (vertical) force of gravity. Shake the table slightly to simulate horizontal earthquake ground motions and the structure will more often than not come tumbling down. So it is with many real buildings in earthquake-prone areas (Figure 3.7), and it is not just the buildings – heavy furniture, such as bookcases, shelving and cupboards, is often placed in buildings with little if any thought given to what might happen to anyone sitting next to or lying beneath the furniture if an earthquake were to subject it to sideways motions.

It is possible to build structures and to configure their internal layout and furnishing to resist earthquake ground motions. There are a number of fundamental principles in aseismic (earthquake-resistant) construction, in particular:

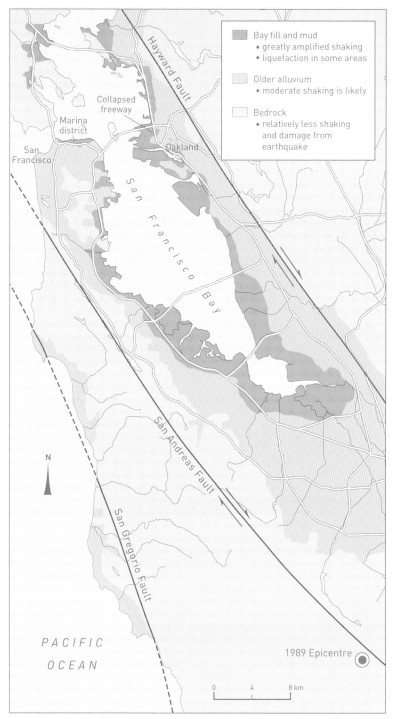

Figure 3.4 Surface geology of the San Francisco Bay area and its influence on ground motion in the (M=6.9) 1989 Loma Prieta earthquake. The Marina district was particularly badly affected. **Source:** Keller, Edward A.; Devecchio, Duane E., *Natural Hazards: Earth's processes as hazards, disasters and catastrophes*, 3rd edition, © 2012, p. 66. Reprinted by permisson of Pearson Education Inc., Upper Saddle River, NJ.

- structural regularity and symmetry
- strong connectivity between different structural elements (e.g. walls and floors)
- use of strong, flexible and ductile materials
- ease of exit
- good workmanship
- fire resistance.

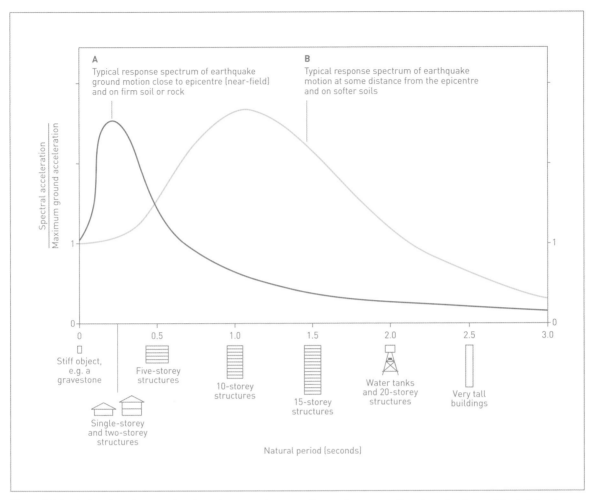

A
Typical response spectrum of earthquake ground motion close to epicentre (near-field) and on firm soil or rock

B
Typical response spectrum of earthquake motion at some distance from the epicentre and on softer soils

Spectral acceleration
Maximum ground acceleration

Stiff object, e.g. a gravestone

Five-storey structures

Single-storey and two-storey structures

10-storey structures

15-storey structures

Water tanks and 20-storey structures

Very tall buildings

Natural period (seconds)

Figure 3.5 Typical earthquake ground motions close to and at some distance from an earthquake epicentre, and the building types they affect. The longer the natural period of wave motion the lower the wave frequency. **Source:** Coburn and Spence, 2002.

Figure 3.6 Effects of earthquake induced soil liquefaction. The sheet of sandy sediment was deposited on fields in the epicentral area of an earthquake affecting the northern Nile valley, Egypt, by fountains of water that issued from the ground during the event. The farmers were mainly concerned about the loss of crops and the burial of fertile top soil. **Photo:** Martin Degg.

Figure 3.7 Mexico City, 1985. a) Catastrophic building failure through inadequate resistance to horizontal (shearing) earthquake ground motions. The lower part of the structure has withstood the motions because of the bracing effect of adjacent buildings. This in turn will have compounded the stresses experienced in the upper part of the structure. b) Damage caused by pounding effect between (inadequately spaced) adjacent buildings subject to horizontal ground motions. **Photos:** Martin Degg.

Figure 3.8 The importance of regularity to aseismic construction is demonstrated in the structure of this hotel under construction in Mexico City.
Photo: Martin Degg.

Buildings with an asymmetrical (e.g. L-shaped) profile or plan form have often proved less resistant to earthquakes than those with a more regular (e.g. rectangular, cubic or pyramidal) shape. This is because the different structural units can twist against each other in an earthquake, generating additional stresses and strains at the point of contact between them (Smith and Petley, 2009). Regularity should also be sought in terms of the internal stiffness of the building, with areas of potential weakness (e.g. window openings) distributed as regularly as possible through the structure to ensure that it responds uniformly to shearing motions. Similarly, zones of strength (e.g. stairwells, elevator shafts) should, wherever possible, be situated centrally in the core of a building (see Figure 3.8) . Figure 3.9 shows these principles applied to the construction of three of the world's most famous earthquake-proof skyscrapers:

the TransAmerica Building in San Francisco, the US Bank Tower in Los Angeles and Taipei 101 in Taiwan. Steel framing is frequently used, either internally or externally, because it is ductile and so absorbs shearing motions when violently shaken. Glass on the other hand is brittle, as is masonry (brick walls), so these materials should be used in such a way that they do not compromise the strength of the framework if they disintegrate in an earthquake.

Aseismic construction is not a new thing. There is a growing body of evidence showing that the basic principles of earthquake-resistant design were developed in a range of societies before the modern industrial age, and that these principles were reflected in traditional building practices and cultural adaptations to earthquake hazard. Some of these adaptations continue to be applied today; others are known to us only through

25

Figure 3.9 Famous earthquake resistant skyscrapers: a) US Bank Tower (formerly Library Tower), Los Angeles, USA; b) Taipei 101, Taipei, Taiwan; c) TransAmerica Building, San Francisco, USA. **Photos:** Clinton Steads, Francisco Diez, eirikref/Flickr (Creative Commons licence).

archaeological evidence from once great (urban) civilisations. For example, Figure 3.10 shows examples of Mayan architecture from the seismically active area of south-east Mexico, Guatemala and western El Salvador and Honduras in Central America. The Maya, together with the Aztecs and the Inca, were among the dominant American-Indian groups prior to the European colonial conquests from the 16th century onwards. Comparison of Figures 3.8, 3.9 and 3.10 suggests that the Maya had developed a relatively sophisticated understanding of the importance of building symmetry and regularity to seismic resistance.

Similar understanding seems to have existed within the Aztec empire, where pyramidal structures were commonplace, and in the Inca empire 2000 miles to the south, centred on what is now Peru in South America (Kovach, 2004). Inca stone architecture is similar to that of the Maya and, in addition, the Inca developed a method of constructing very strong houses in rural areas using walls made from a latticework of interwoven canes plastered with mud. This technique, called Quincha

or basket-weave construction, helps to tie the main structural elements of houses together in a very ductile manner, giving them resistance to shearing earthquake motions. Unfortunately much of this indigenous knowledge in Latin America was lost through the process of colonisation by European powers (Oliver-Smith, 1994), so one key hazard management challenge today is to find ways of reintroducing it into societies (see Figure 3.11). We discuss ways in which this might be achieved in Chapter 6.

Fire is a secondary hazard linked to earthquake impact, and one that can make a major contribution to the total amount of damage caused. In the 1906 San Francisco earthquake, approximately 10km² of the central part of the city, including the entire central business district, was razed to the ground by fire. The fires were mainly started by cooking and heating stoves setting the debris from wooden buildings alight, but the vulnerability of the city was compounded by the widespread fracture of water mains that made it difficult to pump water into the affected areas in sufficient volumes to extinguish the fires (Zeilinga de

Boer and Sanders, 2005).

In the Great Kanto (Tokyo–Yokohama) earthquake of 1923, firestorms (wind-driven fires) destroyed half the city, incinerating up to 150,000 people. The city's acute vulnerability to fire was due to the dominance of wooden buildings with highly combustible furnishings (e.g. straw mats, oiled paper wall panels) and the widespread use of open charcoal fires and cooking stoves in homes – the earthquake struck at lunch time (Mitchell, 1999).

In the century that has followed these events, the switch from wooden to predominantly concrete and brick construction has done much to reduce global urban vulnerability to fire following an earthquake, as has the use of new types of heating and cooking fuel (e.g. electricity, and gas piped from self-contained tanks on building roofs rather than through underground pipes susceptible to fracture). Modern building and planning regulations are designed to minimise the risk of fire spreading from one building to the next, and urban water systems can be designed to ensure emergency supply in times of crisis. For

Figure 3.10 Examples of Mayan architecture showing the symmetry and regularity required for earthquake resistance. **Photos:** GollyGforce/Flickr and kuma chan/Flickr (Creative Commons licence).

example, San Francisco now has cisterns and reservoirs to store water, and a system of saltwater pumping stations around the Bay Area. But it is impossible to eliminate the risk from fire completely, and with new types of energy comes the potential for new types of secondary hazard. The 2011 Sendai earthquake off the east coast of Japan, for example, set in motion a string of events that cut off the supply of cooling water to several of the country's nuclear power plants, eventually leading to fire, explosions and the risk of nuclear meltdown at the Fukushima plant 240km north of Tokyo. This caused widespread international concern, and the need to evacuate over 5000 people from within a 30km (19 mile) radius of the crippled plant, where the earthquake itself had caused relatively little significant damage.

Other human factors contributing to vulnerability

A range of social factors contribute to human vulnerability to earthquake hazard (Birkmann, 2006). Most obvious, perhaps, is age insofar as senior citizens and babies/very young children tend to be less mobile and therefore less able to respond quickly in exiting a building once it starts to shake in an earthquake. Elderly residents can also prove more reluctant to leave property and possessions behind, while the youngest family members are often reliant on parents or older children to direct them. Linked to this dependency of the oldest and youngest family members is the observation from many earthquake disasters that the death toll among married women is higher than that among men (Halvorson and Parker Hamilton, 2007). Mothers in many societies are more likely to take the lead in helping babies, infants and parents to leave a building, and so are more likely to be delayed in their own evacuation (Degg and Homan, 2005). In societies where women continue to assume traditional maternal roles, women typically spend more time in the family home than men, so the likelihood of them being caught indoors when an earthquake strikes is greater. Cultural sensitivities can compound the vulnerability of women. For example, in some Middle Eastern countries it would be considered inappropriate for a male earthquake survivor to try to assist a female victim in a distressed/dishevelled state if she was not his wife or a close family member.

Poverty and social class can also be key determinants of human vulnerability to earthquakes (Smith and Petley, 2009). Poorer people, particularly in developing countries, are far more likely to inhabit sub-standard buildings, often situated (in the case of the poorest society members) on marginal land (see Information Box 1.2) that is most exposed to earthquake hazard, such as the steeper slopes surrounding a major city that are susceptible to earthquake-triggered landsliding, or low-lying sections of coastal plain susceptible to amplified earthquake ground motions, liquefaction or tsunami inundation. Poverty, however, is a relative measure and vulnerability is multifaceted, so it cannot always be assumed that the poorest people in any given society will prove the most vulnerable. In the 1992 Dashur earthquake in northern Egypt, for example, the single greatest tragedy was the loss of a multi-storey apartment block in one of Cairo's most affluent northern suburbs. This tragedy occurred because the rich owners had added six extra storeys to the building and removed supporting walls from some of the lower floors without attracting the attention of local building inspectors (Figure 3.12). In the 1993 Latur earthquake in the Maharashtra province of north-central India, people of the Lamani (Banjara) tribe, some of the poorest and most marginalised people in India's entrenched caste (social class) system and often referred to as the 'Gypsies of India', experienced little loss because

Figure 3.11 Oscar Huarcaya is an entrepreneur trained by the charity Practical Action, working on earthquake-resistant housing (improved Quincha). He lives in the Alto Mayo region of northern Peru with his family. Various techniques are used to improve the traditional quincha technology such as using concrete foundations, treating the timber against wood rot and insect infestation and using lightweight roofsheets which reduce the danger of falling tiles. **Photo:** © Practical Action/Chris Martin.

the flimsy tent structures they inhabited on waste ground posed no threat to them as the earth shook. Meanwhile, thousands of people from higher castes in the towns and villages of the region were killed as their masonry dwellings constructed of thick stone walls (bonded with mud) and heavy timber roofs collapsed, burying them alive as they slept.

Earthquake hazard mitigation

Approaches to earthquake hazard mitigation fall into a number of broad categories:

- long-term forecasting and short-term prediction
- hazard zonation and associated land-use planning and building regulation
- emergency response preparedness.

These categories embrace responses geared to work over the short term (days to weeks), intermediate term (months to decades) and long term (decades to centuries), as well as the immediacy of emergency disaster response.

The primary objective of earthquake forecasting and prediction is to provide people with a warning to enable them to prepare for an imminent earthquake (medium and longer-term) or to evacuate to safe locations in the days and hours before a damaging event (short-term). Longer-term forecasting has proved relatively straightforward in many tectonic environments, and is based on the premise that stress accumulates through plate movement at a relatively constant rate along many plate boundaries, and so must be released by a regular pattern of seismicity. Analysis of the instrumental (1900–) and historical (pre-1900) records of earthquake activity from tectonic zones allows seismologists to identify patterns in earthquake occurrence, to link these to rates of plate movement to calculate recurrence intervals for events of different magnitude, and to identify seismic gaps that appear overdue for a major earthquake strike. There have been a number of successful forecasts of the general location of medium–high magnitude earthquakes using such methods in recent decades, but these have not always resulted in an effective response.

Figure 3.12 Increased vulnerability to earthquake hazard in an affluent district of Cairo generated through the illegal addition of extra building storeys. **Photo:** Martin Degg.

Figure 3.13, for example, shows the distribution of the larger (medium-magnitude) earthquakes that occurred along Turkey's North Anatolian Fault Zone during the second half of the 20th century. This fault, like the San Andreas Fault in California, is a right lateral strike-slip fault system along which the Anatolian microplate to the south moves west relative to the massive Eurasian plate to the north. In the 1980s Turkish seismologists noted that since 1930 there had been a general migration of epicentres of the largest events along the fault from east to west, almost as though the fault were 'unzipping' as each successive event transferred stress further west (Toksoz *et al.*, 1979). On the basis of this pattern they forecast that the part of the fault system most likely to experience the next large earthquake was the section around the Sea of Marmara, which is one of Turkey's most densely populated and most heavily industrialised areas. It was no surprise to them, then, when the (M=7.6) Izmit earthquake occurred in 1999, centred beneath the eastern shoreline of the sea. Unfortunately the Turkish authorities proved far less well prepared, in terms of both

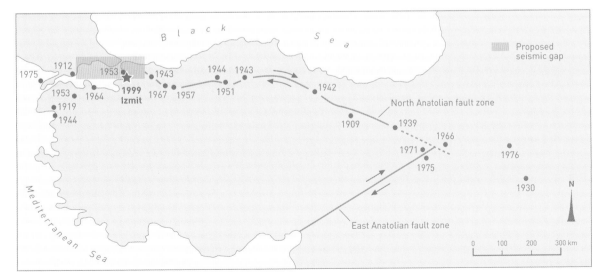

Figure 3.13 Migration of significant earthquake activity along the North Anatolian Fault of Turkey. **Source:** Reprinted from *Tectonophysics*, 85, 1–2, Purcaru, G. and Berckhemer, H., 'Regularity patterns and zones of seismic potential for future large earthquakes in the Mediterranean region', pp. 1–30, © (1982) with permission from Elsevier.

longer and short-term responses, to this forecasted event. Too many buildings proved to be inadequately designed and constructed to resist the seismic ground motions experienced, including many public buildings housing essential emergency services like hospitals. It then took days to get essential emergency relief equipment (e.g. heavy lifting gear, bulldozers) into the affected area, despite its close proximity to major population centres such as Istanbul, just 80km away. This ineffective response to a forecasted event contributed to a death toll of over 17,000 people, with 250,000 made homeless.

One reason that earthquake forecasts are sometimes met with lukewarm response is the fear, among the scientific community as much as among public decision-makers and administrators, of the ramifications of a false alarm. One such forecast, made in 1980 nine months ahead of an anticipated earthquake strike date for a seismic gap off the coast of southern Peru, is estimated to have cost the Peruvian economy over US$50 million (Smith, 2001). A large (M=8.4) earthquake did eventually occur in this gap, killing 75 people and causing estimated losses of US$400 million – but not until June 2001. Such concerns are even more acute when it comes to trying to make short-term earthquake predictions, on the basis of which people might be expected to evacuate homes, workplaces might be temporarily shut down and rescue services put on an emergency footing, Short-term prediction involves recognising and monitoring precursory activity, known to occur in the days and hours leading up to a significant earthquake. A key problem here is that, to date, there is no universally recognised earthquake precursor or set of precursors, and that some major earthquakes have occurred without obvious precursors. Environmental indicators that are monitored and that have been linked to earthquakes in the past

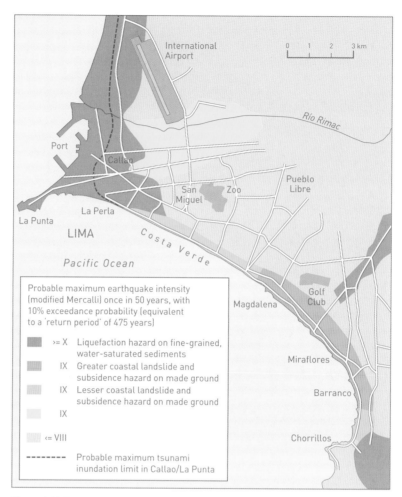

Figure 3.14 Earthquake hazard microzonation for part of Lima and the port of Callao, Peru. **Source:** Degg and Chester, 2005.

include: seismic swarm foreshock activity (concentrations of minor tremors), ground deformation, radon gas emission, changing water levels in wells and abnormal animal behaviour. Japan has one of the world's most sophisticated national earthquake prediction and warning systems, involving over 100 stations that monitor indicators of this type continuously. Despite this, Japanese scientists were unable to provide warning of the 1995 Kobe earthquake, which killed over 5000 people, or the 2011 Sendai earthquake and ensuing tsunami, with an estimated combined death toll of approximately 20,000 people. Reliable short-term earthquake prediction therefore remains an elusive but highly desirable objective.

Hazard zonation is a longer-term response to the problem of earthquakes, based on the mapping of variation in exposure to primary and secondary earthquake hazards. This mapping is conducted at a variety of scales, from global and national (macrozonation) to local (microzonation), and typically provides a measure of the severity of ground shaking experienced in the past (postscriptive assessment) or to be expected in the future within a given period of time and level of probability (predictive assessment). The strength of ground motion is usually defined in terms of earthquake intensity (see Figure 3.3) or better still as peak horizontal ground acceleration, expressed as a percentage of the acceleration due to gravity ($980cm/s^2$). Most probabilistic assessments are based on a 50-year timeframe with a 10% probability that the level of hazard will be achieved within any given 50-year period. This, in effect, represents a 1-in-475-year recurrence interval (Bryant, 2005). The hazard is specified using a 50-year time period because this is assumed to relate to the average life expectancy of a modern engineered structure.

Figure 3.14 shows an earthquake hazard microzonation for part of Lima and its port area of Callao, situated adjacent to the Peru–Chile plate subduction zone on the Pacific rim of South America. The zonation was produced by combining information on ground conditions and observed earthquake and tsunami effects in the city with earthquake probability estimates based on the earthquake record of this part of the Pacific. Maps such as this provide an ideal basis on which to build a longer-term proactive response to the earthquake threat, by ensuring hazard-conscious development and the formulation of emergency response procedures (e.g. for tsunami evacuation). They are, however, only effective if they are accompanied by clear land use and building regulations, and consistent communication and enforcement of these over the long time intervals that can separate any two destructive earthquake events. They can provide a means of delivering effective emergency response in times of disaster by ensuring that key response services (e.g. fire brigade, police) are not located in the most hazardous areas, and through public information schemes aimed at raising awareness of what to do in times of disaster (e.g. evacuation routes to escape possible tsunami waves).

Conclusion

The relationship between human societies and earthquakes is a distinctive one among the suite of natural hazards, insofar as the natural process of earthquake ground shaking poses little or no threat to healthy human beings sitting out in the open. The vast majority of people who fall victim to earthquake ground motions (as opposed to secondary effects such as earthquake-triggered tsunami or landsliding activity) are killed or injured by elements of the human-built environment falling upon them. On the face of it, the solutions to this particular hazard management problem would therefore appear to be more within our control than those of almost any other natural hazard. Yet earthquakes continue to be one of the most costly of natural hazards, in human and economic terms, in rich and poor countries around the world. Part of the reason for this is the sheer magnitude of the problem: so many parts of the world are exposed to earthquake hazard, to a lesser or greater extent, and within these areas live billions of people in tens of millions of buildings with different earthquake sensitivities. Another part of the problem is the large areas and numbers of buildings that can be affected by a single event, but perhaps the most significant issue is science's inability to provide short-term warnings of impending earthquake strike, enabling people to prepare and evacuate buildings if necessary. For the foreseeable future, then, the only realistic approach to reducing earthquake vulnerability is one that adopts a longer-term perspective, with an emphasis on building and organising daily lifestyles for safety. This is a theme we return to in Chapter 6.

Extra resources to accompany this chapter are available on the Top Spec web pages. See page 4 for further information.

ACTIVITY BOX 3

1   Look at videos of the ground shaking during the Christchurch and Sendai earthquakes (available on YouTube). Explain why the ground shaking was so major in Christchurch and assess the contribution it made to the widespread destruction of the city centre.

2   Research the Haiti (2010), Kobe (2005) and Bam (2003) earthquakes. Assess the role that building styles may have played in contributing to the disasters.

3   Research the 2005 Kashmir earthquake. How did poverty add to the scale of this disaster?

4   Using the data in Figure 3.1, plot a scattergraph to explore the relationship between earthquake magnitude (M) and human fatalities.

References

Birkmann, J. (ed) (2006) *Measuring Vulnerability to Natural Hazards: Towards disaster resilient societies.* Tokyo: UNU Press.

Bryant, E. (2005), *Natural Hazards* (2nd edition), Cambridge: Cambridge University Press.

Coburn, A. and Spence, R. (2002) *Earthquake Protection* (2nd edition). Chichester: Wiley.

Degg, M.R. and Chester, D.K.C. (2005) 'Seismic and volcanic hazards in Peru: changing attitudes to disaster mitigation', *The Geographical Journal*, 171, 2, pp. 125–45.

Degg, M.R. and Homan, J. (2005) 'Earthquake vulnerability in the Middle East', *Geography*, 90, 1, pp. 54–66.

Halvorson, S.J. and Parker Hamilton, J. (2007) 'Vulnerability and the erosion of seismic culture in mountainous Central Asia', *Mountain Research and Development*, 27, 4, pp. 322–30.

Keller, E.A. and Devecchio, D.E. (2012) *Natural Hazards: Earth's processes as hazards, disasters and catastrophes* (3rd edition). Upper Saddle River, NJ: Pearson.

Kovach, R.L. (2004) *Early Earthquakes of the Americas*. Cambridge: Cambridge University Press.

Mitchell, J.K. (ed) (1999) *Crucibles of Hazard: Mega-cities and disasters in transition*. Tokyo: UNU.

Murck, B.W.; Skinner, B.J. and Porter, S.C. (1997) *Dangerous Earth: An introduction to geologic hazards*. Chichester: Wiley.

Oliver-Smith, A. (1994) 'Peru's five hundred year earthquake: vulnerability in historical context' in Varley, A. (ed) *Disasters, Development and Environment*. Chichester: Wiley, pp. 31–48.

Purcaru, G. and Berckhemer, H. (1982) 'Regularity patterns and zones of seismic potential for future large earthquakes in the Mediterranean region', *Tectonophysics*, 85, pp. 1–30.

Smith, K. (2001), *Environmental Hazards: Assessing risk and reducing disaster* (3rd edition). London: Routledge.

Smith, K. and Petley, D. (2009) *Environmental Hazards: Assessing risk and reducing disaster* (5th edition). Abingdon: Routledge.

Toksoz, M.N., Shakal, A.F. and Michael, A.J. (1979) 'Space–time migration of earthquakes along the North Anatolian fault zone and seismic gaps', *Pure and Applied Geophysics*, 117, pp. 1258–70.

Zeilinga de Boer, J. and Sanders, D.T. (2005) *Earthquakes in Human History: The far-reaching effects of seismic disruptions*. Princeton, NJ: Princeton University Press.

 Extra resources to accompany this chapter are available on the Top Spec web pages. See page 4 for further information.

4. The tsunami hazard

What are tsunami?

Tsunami are potentially devastating waves in oceans, seas and occasionally lakes. They are a secondary hazard that can result from a number of primary hazards. Tsunami form when a large volume of water is instantaneously displaced. Several different physical processes are capable of this (Figure 4.1).

Tsunami magnitude is related to the volume of water displaced. High-magnitude tsunami which cause widespread destruction most often result from submarine earthquakes. However, there are exceptions:

- The 1883 eruption of Krakatoa, Indonesia, claimed at least 36,000 lives. The final eruption phases blew the volcanic island of Krakatoa apart, blasting huge volumes of volcanic rock, ash and gas into the sea. The tsunami waves, some more than 40m high, devastated coastal settlements on nearby Java and Sumatra.
- Tsunami-deposited sediments nine metres higher than current high tide levels on the east coast of Scotland provide radiocarbon-dated evidence for the vast underwater Storegga slide which occurred between Norway and Iceland around 7300 years ago. Coastal eastern Scotland was then populated by a small number of Mesolithic hunter-gatherers but their landscape, and possibly their lives, may have been devastated by the tsunami (Bondevik et al., 2003; Ward, 2001).

It is important to recognise the difference between tsunami waves and ocean waves. These differences are summarised in Figure 4.2. Tsunami waves usually occur not as a single wave but as a series of waves or 'wave train'.

Open-ocean tsunami travel at tremendous speed. Their small wave heights and long wavelengths mean they are not generally noticed out at sea. Only when tsunami waves approach the coast do their characteristics change and take on their potentially deadly nature.

Earthquake-generated tsunamis

Submarine earthquakes within subduction zones at destructive plate boundaries are often tsunamigenic. As one tectonic plate subducts beneath another, tremendous strain can build up over time. Friction between plates prevents movement until the strain becomes too great, leading to sudden plate motion and vertical

Primary hazard	Tsunami causes
Earthquakes	Sub-sea earthquakes cause vertical movement of the seabed. The jolting of the seabed either upwards or downwards displaces water, which generates a tsunami.
Volcanoes	On volcanic islands, the collapse of a volcanic cone or flank into the water, causing displacement.
Landslides	Coastal or lakeside landslides displacing water and generating a tsunami wave. The collapse of ice from ice sheet and glacier margins can have a similar effect.
Undersea landslides	Landslides can occur on the seabed and generate tsunami. Such landslides are often triggered by earthquakes.
Meteorite/asteroid impact	Very rare, but rather like throwing a stone into a pond.

Figure 4.1 Causes of tsunami.

	Wind-generated ocean waves	Tsunami waves
Wavelength	Up to 100m	Over 100km
Wave height (amplitude)	0.5–5m is typical	Typically less than 1m
Speed in open, deep water	Up to 50km/h	Up to 950km/h

Figure 4.2 Tsunami waves compared to ocean waves.

INFORMATION BOX 4.1 TSUNAMI CONFUSION

The word tsunami is of Japanese origin translating as 'harbour wave'. This reflects the fact that tsunami are at their most dangerous in the shallow, enclosed coastal waters of bays and harbours. The commonly used term 'tidal wave' is very misleading as tsunami have nothing to do with tides. Tides are the daily rise and fall of water caused by the gravitational pull of the moon. Normal ocean waves are caused by friction between the water surface and wind, which is very different to the processes that generate tsunami.

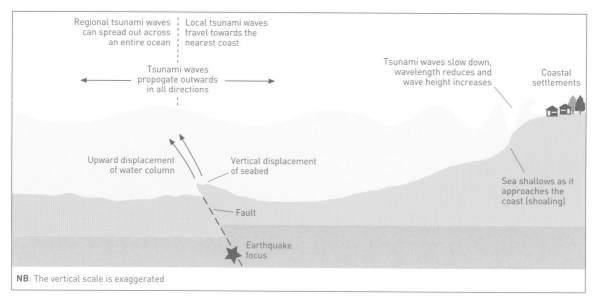

Figure 4.3 Earthquake-generated tsunami.

heaving of the sea bed. Figure 4.3 shows how submarine earthquakes generate tsunami.

Some very large earthquakes do not generate tsunami because the fault movements are horizontal not vertical, so the seabed is not displaced. Large tsunami are usually generated by earthquakes which:

- have a shallow focus, of less than 70km below the seabed
- have magnitudes of 7.0 or higher
- displace the seabed vertically by 1m or more over a wide area
- rupture along the fault surface (tear along the fault) relatively slowly.

Open ocean compared to the coastal zone

As has been already noted, even very large tsunami are barely noticeable to the naked eye in the open ocean. As the waves approach a coast, they alter dramatically as the sea shallows. Figure 4.4 shows how wave velocity and wavelength decrease in shoaling water. As wavelength falls, wave height rises from perhaps only a few centimetres to many metres.

Some tsunami exhibit a characteristic called drawback. If the trough of a tsunami wave

Depth (metres)	Velocity (km/h)	Wave length (km)
7000	943	282
4000	713	213
2000	504	151
200	159	48
50	79	23
10	36	10.6

Figure 4.4 Changes to tsunami waves in shoaling water. **Source:** Intergovernmental Oceanographic Commission, 2008.

reaches the coast before the crest, the sea drains away from the coast, exposing the seabed minutes before the first wave crest arrives. Drawback was widely reported during the 2004 Asian tsunami.

As tsunami waves reach the shore, the effect is much more like a flood than a wave. A normal breaking wave runs up the beach (the swash) and then drains back to sea (the backwash) within a few seconds. Tsunami waves, being much larger, push huge volumes of water onshore, often hundreds of metres inland, flooding wide areas. The force of this pushing water can easily move boats and cars, and destroy homes and other buildings.

In addition, the tsunami wave train means successive waves occur, with the first wave not always the largest. The greater the tsunami wave height at the coast, the greater the destruction is likely to be. However, the physical nature of the coastline influences the impacts of tsunami:

- Cliffs protect coasts from tsunami, whereas low-lying coasts and beaches allow tsunami to flood inland.
- Barrier islands and offshore reefs can force tsunami waves to break some distance from the main shoreline, reducing wave height.
- Coastal ecosystems such as mangroves, swamps and forests will slow down and break up tsunami waves.

- Bays and harbours tend to concentrate wave power and increase wave height, causing greater destruction at the head of the bay.

In addition, some tsunami may remain as localised phenomena if they originate within a partially enclosed sea, such as the Sea of Japan. The enclosed nature of such seas prevents waves from entering wider ocean basins.

Tsunami warning systems

The earthquakes which generate tsunami cannot be predicted, but the size, speed and probable extent of a tsunami can be. The Pacific Tsunami Warning Centre (PTWC) was established in Hawaii in 1949. Tsunami warning systems use an array of technology:

- seismometers to pinpoint the location and size of submarine earthquakes that could be tsunamigenic
- tide gauges to pick up displacements in sea level

- since the mid 1990s, Deep Ocean Assessment and Reporting of Tsunami (DART) buoys in the oceans to detect the passage of a tsunami wave and relay its characteristics to the PTWC via satellite.

Before DART buoys, the magnitude of a tsunami could not be estimated although the timing of its arrival at a particular coast could be. Figure 4.5 shows the travel times predicted by the National Oceanographic and Atmospheric Administration (NOAA) for the February 2010 Chilean tsunami. Locations around the Pacific which could be affected by a tsunami get many hours of warning – ample time for evacuation, assuming that the warnings are clear and can be disseminated widely to people at risk and that people know how best to respond.

In February 2010 tsunami waves reached coastal areas of Chile around 30 minutes after a magnitude 8.8 earthquake. They caused extensive damage and were

responsible for many of the 500+ deaths and estimated $30 billion in property damage. Run-up heights (the maximum onshore water heights above sea level) of 11m were measured at Constitución in Chile. Across the wider Pacific the tsunami was relatively small, with run-up heights of 1m recorded in New Zealand and Hawaii. Within Chile, the navy (which has responsibility for issuing tsunami warnings) was heavily criticised for not issuing an immediate national tsunami alert. Some Chilean ports issued their own warnings but a national warning never came. Constitución was a mere 150km from the epicentre of the massive earthquake and a clearer warning may have saved lives.

INFORMATION BOX 4.2 CRY WOLF SYNDROME

In March 2010, representatives from the Japan Meteorological Office apologised for wrongly forecasting 3m-high tsunami waves striking Japan from the Chilean earthquake a few days earlier. 1.5 million coastal residents had been urged to evacuate. In the event, the waves that arrived were barely noticeable. Even with modern technology, correctly predicting the magnitude of tsunami from a distant earthquake is very hard. The danger is that too many incorrect alerts eventually lead to 'cry wolf syndrome' – that is, having experienced numerous false alarms, people ignore the alarm when there is real danger. This happened at Hilo on Hawaii in May 1960 when many people ignored tsunami alarms, contributing to 61 deaths when a 5m tsunami hit the coast.

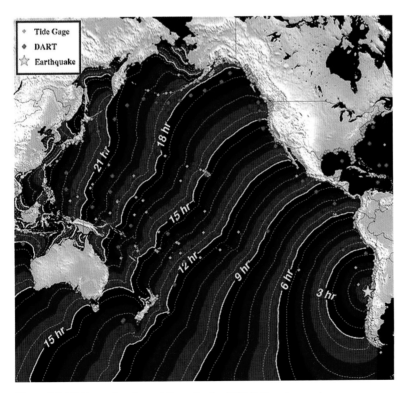

Figure 4.5 NOAA predicted travel times for the 2010 Chilean tsunami.
Source: NOAA, 2010.

Samoa, American Samoa and Tonga were stuck by tsunami waves up to 14m high in September 2009, caused by a magnitude 8.1 earthquake in the Tonga subduction zone at a depth of only 18km. It caused 192 deaths, as well as extensive damage to coastal property. Warnings were issued promptly by the PTWC but dissemination of the warnings was patchy. In Pago Pago (capital of American Samoa), local radio warned people to move inland but many coastal villages did not have siren warning systems. Perhaps more importantly, the waves made landfall only 20 minutes after the earthquake, and only four minutes after the PTWC warning was issued, giving people little time to move to safety. In reality the earthquake ground-shaking was a better warning of the potential for a tsunami. Preparation in the form of education is vital for coastal communities at risk of tsunami, so people can recognise the signs of risk and move to safety.

Tsunami vulnerability

The Boxing Day tsunami of 26 December 2004 was one of the most devastating natural disasters of the last 100 years. It was a highly unusual physical event for a number of reasons:

- The earthquake had a magnitude of 9.3 – one of the largest ever recorded.
- The fault beneath the seabed off Aceh in Indonesia moved for a record 10 minutes, rupturing along a length of over 1500km.

	Indonesia	Sri Lanka	India	Thailand	Myanmar	Maldives
Estimated number of deaths	168,000	35,000	18,000	8000	500	100
Estimated number of displaced people	500,000+	500,000+	650,000	7000	3200	15,000+
Estimated economic cost 2005 (US$)	4 billion	1.5 billion	2.2 billion	0.5 billion	Unknown	1.3 billion

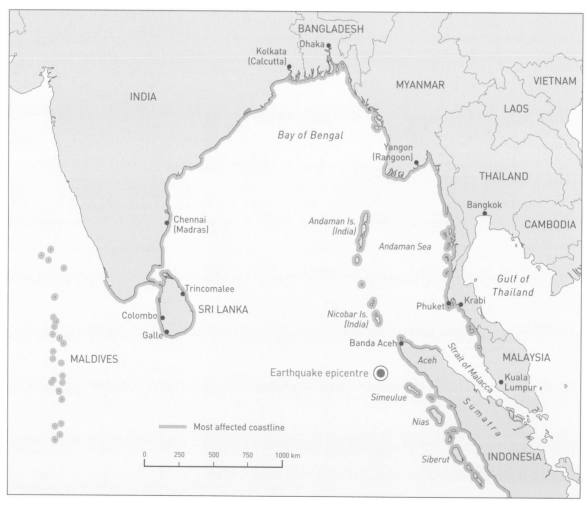

Figure 4.6 Impacts of the 2004 Asian tsunami. **Sources:** USGS website; ReliefWeb website.

- Some parts of the fault may have been displaced by up to 20m.
- At some coastal locations in Indonesia, the tsunami wave was over 20m high – the height of a six-storey building (Birkmann, 2008).

As the tsunami spread out from the Indonesian coast over a period of over 12 hours, it caused fatalities in 14 countries, making this disaster international in scale. So large was the tsunami that it was detected as far away as Mexico and Canada. The event was very low-frequency but very high-magnitude – in many ways this explains the huge toll it took (see Figure 4.6).

The colossal impact of the Asian tsunami (250,000 dead, 10 million displaced/homeless and over US$10 billion in damage) resulted from the vulnerability of many coastal communities in South Asia. Key factors included:

- The lack of a tsunami warning system in the Indian Ocean and lack of tsunami defences.
- High-density coastal populations: many areas have seen rapid population growth and development in the last few decades as coasts are employment centres (tourism, fishing, transport and trade).
- Lack of education and community knowledge of tsunami: only 1–2% of all recorded natural disasters between 1980 and 2007 in Sri Lanka and Indonesia were tsunami, yet over 90% of natural disaster deaths in the same period were from one tsunami (the 2004 event).
- Poorly built homes combined with a lack of hazard zoning, which meant that many buildings were built directly on the shoreline.
- Three of the worst-hit regions – Aceh province in Indonesia, and north and east Sri Lanka – had suffered from years of tension and conflict, diverting resources from the development, education and planning that might have

increased coping capacity in the event of disaster.

The Asian tsunami triggered a huge emergency response, relief and rehabilitation effort which, to date, has amounted to over US$6.3 billion in various forms of aid from governments, NGOs, companies and other organisations. Crucially, a tsunami warning system has been developed for the Indian Ocean led by UNESCO. The Indian Ocean Tsunami Warning System (IOTWS) went live in 2006. The necessary seismographs, DART buoys and satellite communication equipment is now in place but IOTWS will only save lives in the future if:

- local warning dissemination systems are developed which ensure everyone gets a warning
- evacuation routes and safe havens are developed
- community education is developed to help people understand warnings and the actions that need to be taken.

Given the nature of tsunami, coastal property in developing countries will always be at risk due to the immense cost of hard engineering solutions to prevent tsunami damage.

Mitigating tsunami risk

On 12 July 1993 a submarine earthquake of magnitude 7.8 occurred close to Okushiri Island, west of Hokkaido, Japan. The earthquake focus was shallow, only 34km below the seabed, and the epicentre a mere 50km from Okushiri Island. For the 4700 residents of the island the impact of the tsunami was immediate and devastating:

- The first tsunami waves struck just 3–4 minutes after the earthquake.
- Some waves reached a height of 20m+.
- At least 230 people were killed, 200+ injured and damage was estimated at over $600 million.
- The tsunami triggered a major landslide, which buried a hotel, killing 29 people.
- Fires were started as fuel and gas lines ruptured, and some fatalities resulted from these fires.

- The fishing port of Aonae was severely damaged and the small village of Monai was completely destroyed (Hokkaido Tsunami Survey Group, 1993).

The Okushiri disaster illustrates the problem of tsunami which originate close to coastlines. A mere five minutes after the earthquake, the Japanese Meteorological Organisation issued a tsunami warning. This was a rapid response, but Okushiri was so close to the epicentre that the warning came too late.

In response to the 1993 tsunami, a major hazard mitigation programme has been undertaken on Okushiri Island. Since 1993 about $1.1 billion has been spent on tsunami defences, warning and education on Okushiri, amounting to over $250,000 per resident. This includes:

- a 6.6m-high tsunami evacuation platform for the port of Aonae
- a warning system designed to go off only two minutes after an earthquake of magnitude 5 or greater is detected
- personal tsunami alarms for the island's 1700 households, linked to the wider warning system
- 14km of tsunami sea-walls ranging in height from 5m to 12m along the 84km coast
- four automated sluice gates that seal off vulnerable low-lying river mouths when an earthquake is detected
- 40 marked evacuation routes around the island (Hirata and Murakami, 2006).

Okushiri has opted for a highly expensive 'techno-fix' response that relies on hard engineering and the latest electronic communication and warning systems, which few communities around the world can afford. Less costly mitigation is possible (see Figure 4.7), although it relies on maintaining a coastal buffer zone through strict planning regulations that often prove difficult to enforce.

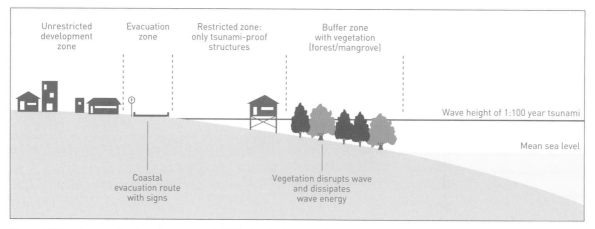

Figure 4.7 Land use zoning to reduce tsunami risk in developing countries.

Conclusion

High-magnitude tsunami are relatively rare. Unlike the earthquakes that most commonly cause them, tsunami can be predicted and effective warnings issued, leading to successful evacuations. Warning and evacuation systems rely on rapid, sometimes global, communication to trigger an alert as well as local dissemination. It is at the local level where these systems are often weak and ineffective. Mitigation through hard-engineering defences is possible, but hugely costly and beyond the means of most coastal populations in the developing world. However, careful land use zoning, maintenance of coastal vegetation and evacuation planning can reduce risk. Even with effective warning, many vulnerable people and their property in developing countries remain at risk in increasingly crowded and ill-planned coastal zones, especially when a tsunamigenic earthquake epicentre is within 100km of the coast.

References

Birkmann, J. (2008) 'Assessing vulnerability before, during and after a natural disaster in fragile regions: case study of the 2004 Indian Ocean tsunami in Sri Lanka and Indonesia', UNU WIDER Research Paper 2008/50. Available online at *www.wider.unu.edu/publications/working-papers/research-papers/2008/en_GB/rp2008-50/_files/79432498624659550/default/rp2008-50.pdf* (last accessed 10 May 2011).

Bondevik, S., Mangerud, J., Dawson, S., Dawson, A. and Lohne, O. (2003) 'Record-breaking height for 8000-year-old tsunami in the North Atlantic', *Eos*, 84, 31, pp. 289–93. Available online at *www.uib.no/People/ngljm/PDF_files/Bondevik-al-03-EOS.pdf* (last accessed 10 May 2011).

Hokkaido Tsunami Survey Group (1993) 'Tsunami devastates Japanese coastal region'. Available online at *http://nctr.pmel.noaa.gov/okushiri_devastation.html* (last accessed 10 May 2011).

Hirata, Y. and Murakami, M. (2006) 'Island hit by 1993 killer tsunami remains vigilant', *The Japan Times Online*, 16 November. Available online at *http://search.japantimes.co.jp/cgi-bin/nn20061116f2.html* (last accessed 10 May 2011).

Intergovernmental Oceanographic Commission (2008) *Tsunami: The Great Waves* (rev. edition). Paris: UNESCO.

ReliefWeb website: *http://reliefweb.int*

United States Geological Survey website: *www.usgs.gov*

Ward, S.N. (2001) 'Landslide tsunami', *Journal of Geophysical Research*, 106, B6, pp. 201–15.

Extra resources to accompany this chapter are available on the Top Spec web pages. See page 4 for further information.

ACTIVITY BOX 4

1 Explain how better community education and preparedness might have reduced the total death toll from the Asian tsunami in 2004.

2 Use the BBC website news archive to produce a timeline of responses to the 2004 Asian tsunami, from 26 December 2004 to the end of January 2005.

3 Explain why tsunami which originate close to populated coastal areas, such as the Chilean tsunami in 2010 and the Okushiri tsunami in 1993, are particularly dangerous.

4 Comment on the approach taken by Okushiri Island to tsunami mitigation. How far is the expense of tsunami warning systems and defences justified in terms of the risk of future tsunami?

5 There are many amateur videos of tsunami, especially the 2004 Asian tsunami, on YouTube and other internet video sites. Viewing some of these is a very useful way to compare tsunami to 'normal' waves.

5. Volcanic hazards

The eruption of Iceland's Eyjafjallajökull in March 2010 proved just how hazardous volcanoes can be in a globalised world. Eyjafjallajökull's ash caused no deaths and only minor inconvenience on Iceland as the volcano is in a sparsely populated area and the ash drifted away from Iceland into the North Atlantic. Conversely, air travel across most of north-west and central Europe was disrupted for around one month as hundreds of flights were cancelled, stranding thousands of people and holiday-makers. Faced with potential damage to sophisticated jet engines if they injested ash, Europe's civil aviation authorities closed airspace for days on end.

Disruption such as this should not surprise us. Worldwide there are some 500 volcanoes that have erupted in recorded history and 50–60 erupt every year. Volcanoes are found in very specific geographical locations. Over 90% of volcanoes occur on plate margins – the remainder being found at isolated mid-plate hot spots. These locations are often highly populated because:

• The relatively flat fringes of volcanic islands and lower slopes of stratovolcanoes have fertile land due to the weathering of volcanic ash.
• Many volcanoes are close to coasts, which in turn are populated and often urbanised due to fishing, trade and transport.
• Awesome volcanic landscapes are popular tourism locations.
• Rapid population growth and urbanisation since the 1960s has often led to the expansion of the poorer districts and unplanned (shanty) developments of overcrowded cities onto the lower slopes of active volcanoes, where land is more freely available.

Estimates suggest that around 10% of the world's population lives within 100km of a volcano which has been active during the last few hundred years. It is perhaps surprising that the impacts of volcanic activity are not greater than the estimates of around 92,000 people killed between 1900 and 1999, with a further 5 million affected. This might be explained by the fact that, unlike earthquakes, volcanoes often provide warnings of eruption, and modern science is increasingly good at monitoring volcanic activity and predicting eruptions.

Measuring volcanic eruptions

Just as the Richter or moment magnitude scales measure the magnitude of an earthquake, volcanologists have devised the volcanic explosivity index (VEI) to measure the size of eruptions. VEI is based on the volume of ejecta (gas, ash, tephra, lava) erupted and how high this is thrown into the atmosphere (plume height) as shown in Figure 5.1.

Eruptions of VEI 0–4 are common. Kilauea, a basaltic shield volcano on the island hot spot of Hawaii, has been erupting more or less continually since 1983. Low VEI eruptions are associated with hot spots and constructive plate margins. Eruptions tend to be of basaltic lava, which has a low gas and silica content. Lava, at a temperature of over 900°C, erupts effusively and forms lava flows. Iceland's basaltic volcanoes such as Eyjafjallajökull tend to be more explosive because of the interaction of magma with ice (from ice caps and glaciers), which generates steam, adding to explosive power.

Higher up the VEI scale (VEI 4–8) eruptions are andesitic and associated with stratovolcanoes at subduction zones (80% of volcanoes

VEI number	Description	Plume height	Ejecta volume	Example
0	Non-explosive	←100m	→1000m³	Mauna Loa, 1984 (Hawaii)
1	Gentle	100–1000m	→10,000m³	Nyiragongo, 2002 (Democratic Republic of Congo)
2	Explosive	1–5km	→1,000,000m³	Tristan da Cunha, 1961 (Atlantic island)
3	Severe	3–5km	→10,000,000m³	Nevado del Ruiz, 1985 (Colombia)
4	Cataclysmic	10–25km	→0.1km³	Eyjafjallajökull, 2010 (Iceland)
5	Paroxysmal	→25km	→1km³	Mount St Helens, 1980 (USA)
6	Colossal	→25km	→10km³	Mount Pinatubo, 1991 (Philippines)
7	Super-colossal	→25km	→100km³	Tambora, 1815 (Indonesia)
8	Mega-colossal	→25km	→1000km³	Yellowstone, 640,000 BP (USA)

Figure 5.1 The volcanic explosivity index.

are of this type). Andesite magma has a higher silica and dissolved gas content than basalt. As such, it generates highly explosive eruptions, although these are rare events with long gaps between eruptions. For example, in August 2010 more than 20,000 people were evacuated from the area around the Mount Sinabung stratovolcano in Indonesia, which previously erupted in 1600.

Volcanic hazard variability

Volcanic hazards are numerous. Hot spot/constructive plate margin shield volcanoes and fissure eruptions tend to generate extensive lava flows with minor ash, gas and tephra eruptions. Stratovolcanoes can produce a wide range of hazards, often occurring in sequence/concurrently in a short space of time (Figure 5.2).

Decade volcanoes

The United Nations designated the 1990s as the International Decade for Natural Disaster Reduction (IDNDR). As part of the focus on understanding risk and reducing vulnerability to natural disasters, 16 'decade volcanoes' were identified to be studied in greater depth. These volcanoes were identified using a number of criteria:

- multiple hazard volcanoes, e.g. pyroclastic flows, lahars and ash fall
- recently active
- close to large population centres, putting many people at risk
- ease of access for scientific study.

Figure 5.3 provides more detail on the decade volcanoes. Thirteen of the 16 decade volcanoes are located at subduction zones and nine of these are within the Pacific Ring of Fire. Many of these volcanoes appear quiet and have not erupted for decades (e.g. Rainier, Vesuvius), whereas others rumble on an almost daily basis (e.g. Sakurajima,

INFORMATION BOX 5.1 KILLER VOLCANIC LAKES

There are also more unusual hazards. In 1986 Lake Nyos in Cameroon 'erupted' a very large volume of carbon dioxide. Being denser than air, the carbon dioxide flowed down into a nearby valley and silently suffocated 1700 people. A similar incident had occurred at Cameroon's Lake Monoun in 1984, killing 37 people. Lake Kivu between Rwanda and the Democratic Republic of Congo is thought to be at risk from a similar event. These gas eruptions are referred to as limnic eruptions or lake overturns.

They are caused when volcanic gases seep upwards through rock fissures from magma below. Gases become dissolved in lake bottom sediments and build up over time. An earth tremor, or sediment slide within the lake, can disrupt the sediments, rapidly releasing the dissolved gas. Since 2001, attempts have been made to continually 'degas' Lakes Nyos and Monoun using pipes running from the lake sediment to the surface. It is hoped this will prevent a dangerous build-up of carbon dioxide.

Pyroclastic flows

Dense downslope surges of volcanic ash and gas moving at up to 600km/h and reaching temperatures of up to 1000°C, they can travel 10–20km from a volcanic vent. Pyroclastic flows account for the majority of volcano deaths through a combination of burning and asphyxiation.

Tephra

Volcanoes eject tiny ash particles (under 2mm), medium-sized lapilli (2–64mm) and volcanic bombs (64mm+). Lava bombs can kill on impact; ash and lapilli build up on roofs, causing collapse, as well as blocking roads and drains. Hot tephra can start fires.

Flank collapse

Very viscous magma (rhyolitic magma) can form an immovable 'plug' within a volcano. Pressure from magma below can cause the side of a volcano to bulge and eventually collapse, leading to a sideways eruption or lateral blast. This is how Mount St Helens erupted in 1980.

Lahars

Mudflows of volcanic ash and other debris occur when tephra and water combine and flow downslope, at speeds of up to 100km/h. Heavy rain, volcano-induced ice and snow melt, or lake outbursts can all trigger lahars. These mudflows can occur months or years after an eruption.

Figure 5.2 Volcanic hazards.

Etna) but occasionally erupt more violently.

For the populations living close to these volcanoes, sometimes numbering hundreds of thousands, there is significant risk. Most of the 16 would erupt deadly pyroclastic flows and generate lahars capable of travelling tens of kilometres from the volcanic summit. In some cases (e.g. Colima or Etna), surrounding populations are largely rural and agricultural, and at relatively low population densities. Evacuating these areas would be possible if the volcano signalled that eruption was likely. In other locations (e.g. Vesuvius), high-density, complex urban areas are at risk. Evacuation of these locations may prove much more problematic.

Monitoring and prediction

The key difference between an earthquake and a volcanic eruption in terms response is the ability to predict, at least with some certainty, volcanic eruptions. Volcanoes exhibit precursor activity, which can be useful in eruption forecasting (Figure 5.4).

Some precursors are visible, such as increased melting of snow and ice; others are more subtle and rely on monitoring using sensitive scientific equipment:

- Seismometers measure tremors, which may indicate movement of magma beneath the volcano.
- Extensometers measure ground deformation and flank bulging.
- Gas spectrometers measure the composition and volume of gas emissions.
- Airborne gravimeters measure the changes in ground density that can indicate upwelling of low-density magma.
- Thermometers and thermal imaging measure changes in lake water and ground temperature.

The technical nature and cost of this equipment mean that not all volcanoes are monitored constantly. Roughly 20 are, mostly in the developed world, such as Mounts Unzen, Etna, Vesuvius and Rainier. Nevertheless, some developing nations have effective monitoring and warning organisations such as the Philippines Institute of Seismology and Volcanology (Phivolcs) and the Centre for Volcanology and Geological Hazard Mitigation (PVMBG) in Indonesia, which send field officers out to monitor volcanoes showing early signs of eruption.

Even when eruptions can be predicted with some accuracy, people may not act on the warnings issued. One of the most successful

Volcano	Last major eruption date	Estimated population at risk	Tectonic location
Avachinsky and Koryaksky (Kamchatka, Russia)	1945 and 2008	200,000 people in nearby city of Petropavlosk	Pacific Ring of Fire
Colima (Mexico)	2005	300,000 within 40km of summit	Pacific Ring of Fire
Etna (Italy)	Ongoing	1 million plus	Mediterranean subduction zone
Galeras (Colombia)	2009	450,000 in nearby city of Pasto	Pacific Ring of Fire
Mauna Loa (Hawaii, USA)	1984	75,000	Hawaiian hot spot
Merapi (Indonesia)	2006	80,000+	Indonesian subduction zone
Nyiragongo (DRC)	2002	Up to 1 million	African rift system
Rainier (USA)	1894	80,000	Pacific Ring of Fire
Sakurajima (Japan)	Ongoing	500,000 people in the city of Kagoshima	Pacific Ring of Fire
Santa Maria (Guatemala)	Ongoing	About 100,000	Pacific Ring of Fire
Santorini (Greece)	1950	14,000+	Mediterranean subduction zone
Taal (Philippines)	1977	Up to 1 million, including parts of Manila	Pacific Ring of Fire
Teide (Canary Islands)	1909	900,000	Canary hot spot
Ulawun (PNG)	Ongoing	Several thousands	Pacific Ring of Fire
Unzen (Japan)	1996	50,000+	Pacific Ring of Fire
Vesuvius (Italy)	1944	600,000+, including much of Naples	Mediterranean subduction zone

Figure 5.3 The 16 'decade' volcanoes.

evacuations was that of Mount Pinatubo in 1991. Phivolcs and the United States Geological Survey (USGS) accurately predicted the eruption of the volcano and ordered the evacuation of 60,000 people from an area up to 40km from the summit. In the event the VEI6 eruption (the second-largest of the 20th century) killed only 600–800 people, although over 100,000 were made homeless. Some people refused to evacuate. Phivolcs found that this was because they:

- underestimated the size of the eruption
- did not want to leave their property, livestock and crops
- had no transport and could not walk long distances
- held the traditional belief that the volcano was a god and would not harm them.

The task of evacuating the area was made harder by the rare coincidence of a major volcanic eruption with a tropical cyclone hitting the same area on the same day. As Mount Pinatubo erupted, a category 3 typhoon (Typhoon Yunya) moved over Luzon Island. Torrential rain combined with volcanic ash so that in some places it was 'raining mud'. Volcanic mud-laden roofs and power lines collapsed, and the torrential rain increased the occurrence of lahars on the volcano's slopes.

Contrast this success story with the much smaller eruption of Nevado del Ruiz, Colombia – active for at least a year prior to its eruption in November 1985. Some monitoring instruments were installed in summer 1985, although volcanologists failed to agree on when an eruption might occur (THE, 1999). A minor eruption on 11 September melted part of the volcano's ice cap, generating a lahar that flowed for 27km – a foretaste of what was to come. Visiting Italian volcanologists warned of a large eruption in October. The main eruption occurred on 13 November, melting the volcano's ice cap and unleashing deadly lahars, which killed at least 21,000 people – most of them in the town of Armero, ironically built on mudflow deposits from an earlier eruption in 1845. Prediction and warning are only useful if they are acted upon.

Hazard risk mapping

One of the most important aspects of reducing death tolls from eruptions is hazard risk mapping. The USGS published its most up-to-date hazard map for Nevado del Ruiz on 15 November 1985 – two days after the deadly lahar-inducing eruption. This shows that risk mapping can be carried out, but just as important is getting the information to people who can act on it in a timely way.

Hazard maps identify areas at risk from different volcanic hazards. Mount Rainier, in Washington State, USA, is an andesitic stratovolcano, capped by 25 glaciers, that last erupted in the mid-19th century.

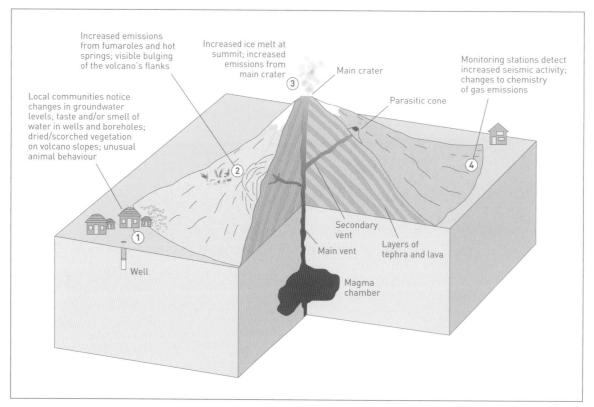

Figure 5.4 Volcano eruption precursors.

Rainier is one of a chain of volcanoes in the Cascades Range (including Mount St Helens) which owe their existence to the Cascadia subduction zone. Figure 5.5 shows the hazard risk map for Mount Rainer:

- a central high-risk zone, up to 20km from the summit, at risk from pyroclastic and lava flows
- an outer lahar-risk zone, within populated river valleys, extending close to 100km from the summit.

Some 80,000 people live in the lahar risk zone. The USGS believes lahars are caused by two processes on Mount Rainer:

1 Lahars generated by glacier meltwater during an eruption phase: as signs of eruption are detected, the rising risk would lead to evacuations.
2 Lahars generated by landslides triggered by the gradual weakening of rocks on Rainier's flanks due to hydrothermal alteration by acid groundwater: these could occur at any time.

The west side of Mount Rainier is believed to be the most unstable, meaning the Puyallup and Nisqually river valleys are most at risk. Risk has been reduced in these areas by:

- drawing up the Mount Rainier Volcanic Hazards Response Plan, which operates at local, county, state and federal levels
- publishing volcanic hazard evacuation routes, which are also signed on roads, leading to high ground
- educating local communities (for instance, schools) on lahar risk and actions that should be taken
- investing in an automated lahar warning system which detects the ground vibration caused by a passing lahar.

The warning system is especially important because a major lahar could reach the town of Orting (population 6000) a mere 40 minutes after it is triggered. Warning sirens in the valleys are tested twice a year

and schools have evacuation drills twice a year. If a lahar is detected, sirens will automatically sound, as will automated warnings on local radio and residents' telephones (so-called 'reverse 911'). Residents are advised to evacuate on foot (cars would cause bottlenecks) and keep 'grab-bags' at home with water, food and first aid supplies. This type of community preparedness is essential if loss of life is to be minimised, although economic losses could still be considerable.

Emergency response

In 2002 Mount Nyiragongo in the Democratic Republic of Congo (DRC) erupted effusively rather than explosively. Erupting basaltic lava, it is one of a number of relatively young but active volcanoes in the African Rift Valley. Nyiragongo is famous for having a long-lived lava lake in its central crater. Nyiragongo had previously erupted in 1977, killing around 70 people (although some estimates suggest this figure was closer to 2000). While in no way explosive, Nyiragongo is paradoxically hazardous because its lava flows at up to 60km/h – more than twice as fast as most people can run.

The 2002 eruption was not unexpected, as increased activity was recorded for several months, but it did proceed very rapidly and was over in less than a day. On 17 January 2002 a 10km+ system of fractures opened up on the south flank of the volcano (see Figure 5.6). These fractures released huge volumes of lava, which quickly flooded through 14 villages, banana fields and crops. Some 350,000 people in Goma (population around 500,000) quickly fled as 15% of the city, including the centre, part of the airport and the homes of up to 120,000, were engulfed. Around 150 people were killed (Allard *et al.*, 2003).

The rapid displacement of so many people created a humanitarian disaster and an urgent need for food, shelter and other aid. About 300,000 people initially fled over the

border into Rwanda, but very quickly moved back into Goma due to the mistrust between Rwandans and Congolese after years of conflict. The emergency relief effort is outlined in Figure 5.7. The relief effort was made more difficult by the closure of Goma airport. Some aid had to be flown to Kinshasa and trucked the 1800km to Goma.

The people of Goma and the other areas of North Kivu affected by Nyiragongo's 2002 eruption were particularly vulnerable to the impacts of a tectonic hazard:

- Conflict in Rwanda in the 1990s had spilled over the border into the DRC, especially into the border town of Goma.
- Many of Goma's population had been displaced by the Rwandan conflict, the First Congo War (1996–97) and the Second Congo War (1998–2003).
- Conflict had gradually eroded the coping capacity of individuals and civil authorities.
- In 2002 over 45% of people in the DRC were under 14 years old and many of these were orphans.
- The human development index had fallen to 0.36, one of the lowest in the world.

Since 2002 the situation in the DRC has barely improved. The ongoing Kivu Conflict has meant that Goma has remained a centre for refugees as well as fighting.

Coping with rising risks

By 2010, the population of Goma had grown to an estimated 800,000 and Gisenyi to 200,000 – meaning that up to 1 million people could be at risk from Nyiragongo's next major eruption. In addition there is the real threat that a future eruption could result in a Lake Nyos-style lake overturn of Lake Kivu (see Information Box 5.1). This could be potentially catastrophic. Scientists estimate Lake Kivu contains 300 million tonnes of dissolved carbon dioxide and 60 million tonnes of dissolved methane (Nayar, 2009).

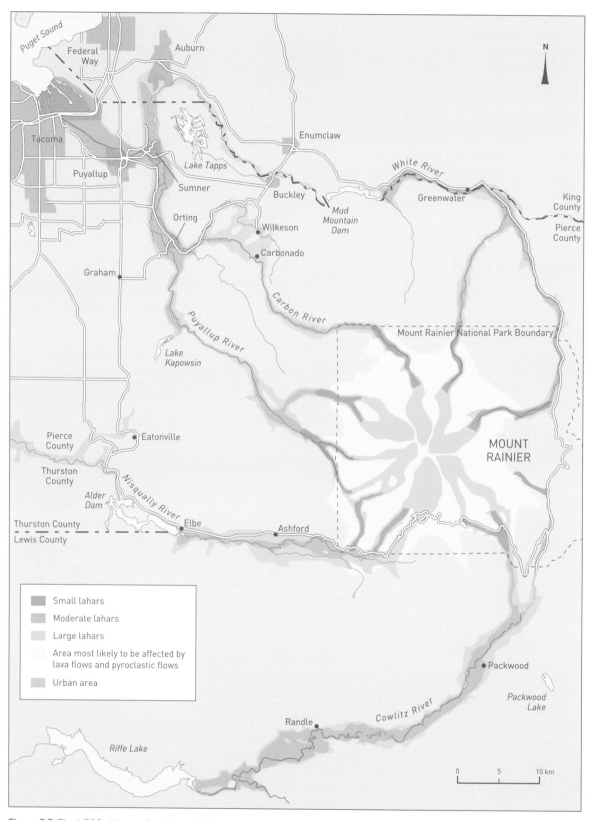

Figure 5.5 The USGS risk map for Mount Rainier. **Source:** Driedger and Scott, 2008.

Up to 2 million people on Kivu's shores could be at risk. While Mount Nyiragongo and its neighbour Nyamuragira erupt visibly and audibly, a lake overturn would be essentially silent and invisible – the carbon dioxide and methane erupted are also odourless.

The risk of a future eruption and/or lake overturn have not gone unnoticed. Improved community preparedness and prediction could save lives and some work has already improved the situation. Under the leadership of the UN Office for the Co-ordination of Humanitarian Affairs (UNOCHA), Goma Volcanic Observatory was updated in 2003 with a network of seven digital seismometers, electronic distance meters and GPS stations. Additional equipment to measure gas composition, heat output and water chemistry was provided. This should mean that some warning of a future eruption can be given. The NGO International Federation of Red Cross and Red Crescent Societies (IFRC) has worked with local community volunteers to increase community preparedness (Figure 5.8).

Diversion and mitigation

A reasonable question to ask might be why didn't the authorities in Goma in 2002 simply divert the lava away from the city? There are several reasons:

- The volume of lava erupted was too large.
- It erupted rapidly from fresh fissures and flowed very quickly.
- The technical and financial challenge would have been too great.

However, some attempts have been made to directly prevent damage and destruction from some volcanic hazards. Nothing can be done to prevent the devastation of pyroclastic flows but some hazards can be 'tamed':

- Concrete and steel reinforced buildings, with pitched roofs, can withstand the build-up of thick tephra fallout.
- Around the highly active Mount Sakurajima in Japan, concrete tunnels have been built to act as shelters from lava bombs.
- In areas of known lahar risk, concrete diversion channels, check dams and sediment traps have been constructed, although these are very costly and only likely to cope with small lahars.

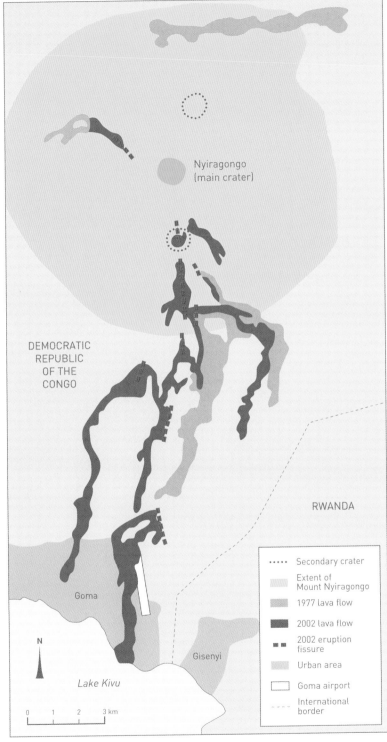

Figure 5.6 The 2002 eruption of Mount Nyiragongo. **Source:** Reproduced with kind permission from Springer Science & Business Media: *Bulletin of Volcanology*, 'Lava flow hazard at Nyiragongo volcano, D.R.C.', 71, 4, 2008, Favalli, M., Chirico, G.D., Papale, P., Pareschi, M.T. and Boschi, E.

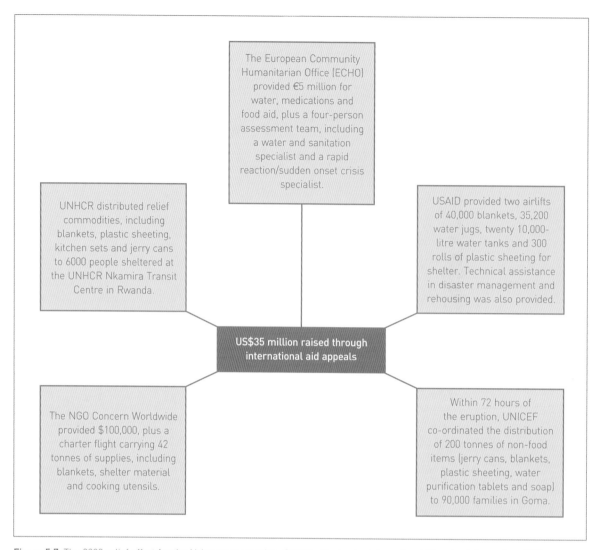

The European Community Humanitarian Office (ECHO) provided €5 million for water, medications and food aid, plus a four-person assessment team, including a water and sanitation specialist and a rapid reaction/sudden onset crisis specialist.

UNHCR distributed relief commodities, including blankets, plastic sheeting, kitchen sets and jerry cans to 6000 people sheltered at the UNHCR Nkamira Transit Centre in Rwanda.

USAID provided two airlifts of 40,000 blankets, 35,200 water jugs, twenty 10,000-litre water tanks and 300 rolls of plastic sheeting for shelter. Technical assistance in disaster management and rehousing was also provided.

US$35 million raised through international aid appeals

The NGO Concern Worldwide provided $100,000, plus a charter flight carrying 42 tonnes of supplies, including blankets, shelter material and cooking utensils.

Within 72 hours of the eruption, UNICEF co-ordinated the distribution of 200 tonnes of non-food items (jerry cans, blankets, plastic sheeting, water purification tablets and soap) to 90,000 families in Goma.

Figure 5.7 The 2002 relief effort for the Nyiragongo eruption. **Source:** Centre for International Disaster Information, 2002

There are two very famous examples of humans attempting to stop lava flows in their tracks. In January 1973 the Eldfell volcano on the Icelandic island of Heimaey erupted. Basaltic lava slowly buried part of the fishing port of Vestmannaeyjar as evacuation of the 5300 people at risk proceeded. By February it was clear that Eldfell's lava flow was likely to block the entrance to the harbour at Vestmannaeyjar. This would have destroyed the economic heart of the island, making repopulation impossible. A plan was hatched. Between February and July 1973, 43 pumps were used to pour millions of gallons of seawater onto the lava flow, eventually stopping it from moving and saving the port.

A different, but ultimately successful, attempt was made on Mount Etna in 1983. Beginning in March 1983, lava from Etna threatened three settlements on the flanks of the volcano. Attempts were made, using explosives, to divert the lava flow by disrupting it. These mostly failed, so bulldozers were used to construct rock embankments to contain the flow in a narrow channel. These succeeded, at a cost of around US$3 million. Had the lava engulfed the settlements, the damage would have cost around US$10 million. When Etna erupted again in 1992 the same embankment tactics were used, this time to save the town of Zafferana (population 7300). In addition an artificial channel was dug, and explosives used to divert two thirds of the lava flow into it and away from the town.

These examples might suggest that humans are capable of controlling volcanic eruptions. However, in both cases the hazard involved small, slow-moving lava flows. In addition the area being 'saved' was small and there was time to plan and adapt plans when things failed to work. In the vast majority of cases humans have very little chance of physically preventing volcanic hazards.

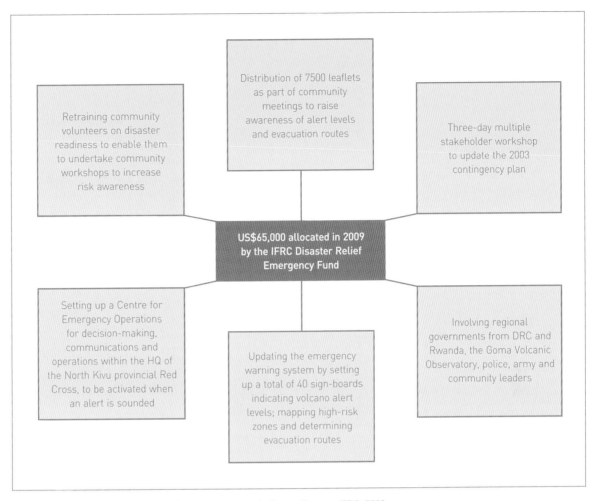

Figure 5.8 The IFRC hazard preparedness programme in Goma. **Source:** IFRC, 2009.

Assessing risk or denying it?

Given the obvious risks of being in close proximity to a potentially devastating volcano, it is surprising to find several of the world's largest cities in such locations. Mexico City sits in the shadow of Popocatépetl, an active stratovolcano only 70km from the city centre.

If ever there was a 'disaster waiting to happen' it is the city of Naples. Naples lies around 15km from Vesuvius. Each year more than 2.5 million tourists walk through the streets of Pompeii, the famous Roman town destroyed when Vesuvius erupted in 79AD. In other words, there is ample evidence of Vesuvius's destructive power close

at hand. The volcano has erupted in living memory. In 1944 four villages on the lower slopes of Vesuvius were destroyed.

Today, up to 3 million people are at risk from a Vesuvian eruption:
- Many homes have been built illegally on the lower and mid slopes of the volcano since the 1944 eruption.
- 600,000 people live in the 18 towns in so-called 'red zone' at greatest risk.
- Estimates suggest it would take three days to evacuate these people, along often narrow and steep, potentially congested roads.

- Current plans assume volcanic precursors will provide a warning of up to four weeks.
- No major evacuation drill has ever been carried out.

In 2003, Italian officials came up with a plan to offer each resident of the red zone €25,000 to move out. This sum was estimated to be about 20–25% of the cost of buying a property elsewhere. Current evacuation plans do not include Naples because they are based on an eruption in 1631 (VEI 4 eruption), which was similar to, but significantly smaller than, the infamous 79AD event (VEI 5 eruption). It is assumed prevailing winds will carry most debris towards the south-east, away from Naples. Other researchers suggest that an eruption like the one in 3780BP (VEI 6 eruption) is an equally likely, but very different, scenario. Figure 5.9 shows the predicted risk from pyroclastic flows if Vesuvius erupts in a similar way to the 3780BP eruption. Pyroclastic flows could surge 20–30km from Vesuvius. The shockwave from these flows could destroy and damage buildings at pressures of over 5Kpa, and ash, gas and heat could cause very high casualties. The impacts could be severe across a large area of Naples. Some scientists have concluded that current risk management regarding Vesuvius is based on optimistic assumptions and a hope that plans work as they should.

Supervolcanoes and mega-disasters

Very high-magnitude, low-frequency volcanic eruptions do happen, but rarely. Eruptions of VEI 6 or greater eject so much ash and gas that they can alter global climate, albeit for a short period (a year or several decades at most). The Mount Pinatubo VEI 6 eruption in 1991 and the eruption of Tambora in 1815 (VEI 7) both had a measurable cooling effect on the Earth's climate as stratospheric volcanic aerosols enveloped the globe, blocking incoming solar radiation.

Modern humans have not experienced the truly cataclysmic impact of a VEI 8 eruption. The most recent such eruption was Taupo on New Zealand's (then unpopulated) north island 26,500 years BP and before that Toba in Indonesia some time between 69,000 and 77,000 years BP. Both of these are classed as supervolcanoes. Today's most famous supervolcano is Yellowstone in the USA, which last erupted 640,000 years ago.

These supervolcanic eruptions were all caldera-forming events. They are recognisable in the landscape today by the presence

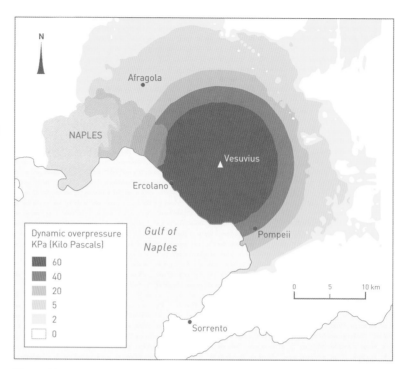

Figure 5.9 Pyroclastic flow risk from Vesuvius. **Source:** Mastrolorenzo *et al.*, 2006. © (2006) National Academy of Sciences, USA.

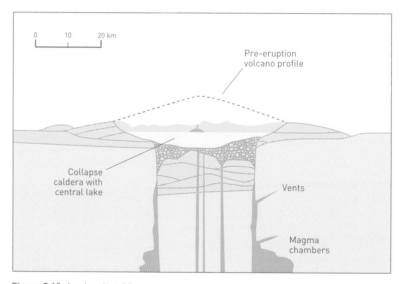

Figure 5.10 A volcanic caldera.

of a central lake surrounded by fragments of a former volcano (Figure 5.10).

Calderas form as vast supervolcanoes begin to erupt, usually from several vents. As the magma chamber empties, the central part of the volcano collapses down into the magma chamber as a circular ring-fracture

forms. Often this collapse phase accompanies a final cataclysmic eruption. So vast are calderas that many, including Yellowstone, have only been identified since the era of satellite remote sensing began. The risk of a supervolcano erupting is low, but further eruptions are inevitable – it is just a question of when. Several very high-magnitude,

Cause	Impacts	Probability
Eruption of the Yellowstone supervolcano, USA	Eruption would devastate an area within 1000km of the caldera, with possibly a 90% fatality rate. Ash fall would blanket 50% or more of the USA. Stratospheric ash and gas would spread around the globe within 10 days. Global climate cooling of 5–10°C is possible, making food production impossible in many locations. Global cooling could last for 6–10 years.	Erupted 0.64, 1.3 and 2.1 million years ago. Eruption interval of 0.6–0.8 million years suggests an eruption should occur in the next 100,000 years.
Collapse of the Cumbre Vieja volcano on La Palma, Canary Islands	Eruption of Cumbre Vieja could cause a catastrophic landslide failure of the volcano's flank into the sea. A mega-tsunami would be generated, fanning out across the Atlantic. Tsunami waves would devastate the Caribbean and the eastern seaboard of the USA. Up to 100 million people around the Atlantic could be affected.	Past eruptions, such as Krakatoa in 1883, have generated tsunami. Sea-floor landslide deposits off La Palma suggest such collapses have occurred in the past. The size of any future collapse, and its timing, are speculative, although future eruptions are certain.

Figure 5.11 Two possible volcanic mega-disasters. **Sources:** Ward and Day, 2001; USGS website.

Worst five by number killed 2001–2010	Disaster	Approx. number killed	Approx. number affected
Earthquakes	Haiti, 2010 (Port-au-Prince)	222,600	3,700,000
	China, 2008 (Sichuan)	87,500	4,600,000
	Pakistan, 2005 (Kashmir)	73,000	5,100,000
	Iran, 2003 (Bam)	30,000	270,000
	India, 2001 (Bhuj)	20,000	6,300,000
Volcanoes	DRC, 2002 (Nyiragongo)	190	400,000
	Colombia, 2008 (Nevado del Huila)	9	104,000
	Yemen, 2007 (Jabal-al-Tair)	6	15
	Ecuador, 2006 (Tungurahua)	5	300,000
	Ethiopia (Arteale)	5	2000
Tsunami (* = combined earthquake and tsunami)	Japan, 2011 (Sendai)*	20,000	400,000
	Indian Ocean, 2004*	230,000	2,300,000
	Indonesia, 2006 (Java)*	800	35,500
	Chile, 2010*	560	2,700,000
	Samoa, American Samoa and Tonga, 2009	200	8500

Figure 5.12 Major geophysical disasters 2001–2011. **Source:** EM-DAT database.

very low frequency volcanic hazards have been identified, which would result in a mega-disaster of global significance (Figure 5.11).

Conclusion

Major volcanic eruptions are relatively rare. Figure 5.12 shows that, for the decade 2001–2011, deaths and numbers affected from the five worst tsunami and five worst earthquakes considerably outnumbered those from the five worst volcanoes. In fact, deaths from volcanic eruptions are relatively rare. This is largely because of improved monitoring and prediction. The scientific equipment used to monitor volcanoes (GPS, laptops, EDMs etc.) has become cheaper and more mobile, so more volcanoes are monitored than ever before. If seemingly quiet volcanoes rumble into life, scientists can be deployed quickly and evacuations organised. The number of people affected by volcanoes can be large. This is due to evacuation and loss of land and property if eruptions occur. Earthquakes occur without warning and, as was outlined in Chapter 4, tsunami can still cause huge problems, especially if they originate close to land.

Volcanic hazards can only very rarely be stopped in their tracks, as has happened on Mount Etna and on Heimaey in Iceland, but improved monitoring, prediction, community education and evacuation plans have significantly reduced risk by moving people out of harm's way in good time.

Extra resources to accompany this chapter are available on the Top Spec web pages.
See page 4 for further information.

ACTIVITY BOX 5

1 Explain why some volcanic eruptions represent a significantly greater physical hazard to human populations than others by contrasting the Nevado del Ruiz event with that of Mount Pinatubo.

2 Describe the science of volcanic eruption prediction. Use information in this chapter and the online United States Geological Survey resource at *http://volcanoes.usgs.gov/about/edu/predict.php*

3 Outline the unusual physical and human circumstances that contributed to the disaster following the eruption of Mount Nyiragongo in the Democratic Republic of Congo in 2002.

4 Use Figure 5.12 and other information in this chapter to consider the extent to which humans have successfully tamed the threat posed by volcanic eruptions.

5 Discuss the fact that Eyjafjallajökull can be described as 'an inconvenient plume' which had a global impact. Research the 2011 Grímsvötn eruption and explain why, although it had a much higher VEI, it had a much lower impact.

References

Allard, P., Baxter, P., Halbwachs, M., Kasareka, M., Komorowski, J.C. and Joron, J.L. (2003) 'The most destructive effusive eruption in modern history: Nyiragongo (RD Congo), January 2002'. Session presented at the EGS-AGU-EUG Joint Assembly, Nice, France, 6–11 April 2003.

Centre for International Disaster Information (2002) *Democratic Republic of the Congo: Volcano Fact Sheet #13.* Available online at *www.cidi.org/report/5387* (last accessed 11 May 2011).

Driedger, C.L. and Scott, W.E. (2008) *Mount Rainier: Living safely with a volcano in your backyard.* US Geological Survey Fact Sheet 2008-3062. Available online at *http://pubs.usgs.gov/fs/2008/3062* (last accessed 11 May 2011).

Favalli, M., Chirico, G.D., Papale, P., Pareschi, M.T. and Boschi, E. (2008) 'Lava flow hazard at Nyiragongo volcano, D.R.C.', *Bulletin of Volcanology*, 71, 4, pp. 363–87.

International Federation of the Red Cross and Red Crescent Societies (IFRC) (2009) *DREF Operation Final Report: Democratic Republic of Congo: Nyiragongo and Nyamuragira volcano eruption alert in Goma.* Geneva: IFRC. Available online at *www.ifrc.org/docs/appeals/09/MDRCD007dfr.pdf* (last accessed 11 May 2011).

Mastrolorenzo, G., Petrone, P., Pappalardo, L. and Sheridan, M.F. (2006) 'The Avellino 3780-yr-B.P. catastrophe as a worst-case scenario for a future eruption at Vesuvius', *Proceedings of the National Academy of Sciences of the United States of America*, 103, 12, pp. 4366–70. Available online at *www.pnas.org/content/103/12/4366.full.pdf+html* (last accessed 11 May 2011).

Nayar, A. (2009) 'Earth science: a lakeful of trouble', *Nature*, 460, pp. 321–3.

Times Higher Education (THE) (1999) 'Deadly deliberation: Nevada del Ruiz, Colombia, 1985', *THE*, 9 April. Available online at *www.timeshighereducation.co.uk/story.asp?storycode=145874* (last accessed 11 May 2011).

Ward, S.N. and Day, S. (2001) 'Cumbre Vieja Volcano: potential collapse and tsunami at La Palma, Canary Islands', *Geophysical Research Letters*, 28, 17, pp. 3397–400.

6. Recent trends and future prospects

There have been significant advances in our understanding of tectonic hazards and risk over the last 20 years, most particularly in conceptualising disaster risk. These advances have, in large part, been driven out of necessity and the stark realisation that human societies continue to be extremely vulnerable to these hazards. In an increasingly globalised and interconnected world this vulnerability is, if anything, greater now than at any time in human history, and there is every likelihood that, unless we find ways of responding more proactively and in a more sustainable manner to tectonic hazards, the 21st century will prove even more calamitous in terms of disaster losses than the 20th century (Huppert and Sparks, 2006). Indeed, there is already a sense of this if one stops to consider some of truly horrific tectonic hazard impacts recorded from around the world in the first decade of this century. The international community, and in particular the United Nations, has been at the forefront of efforts to try to ensure a more effective (global) response to the threat of all so-called natural disasters generally, but in particular earthquakes, volcanoes and tsunami. In this concluding chapter we look at the development in understanding of the nature of this challenge over a 20-year period (1990–) as reflected in the disaster mitigation agenda of the UN, and then project forward to identify emerging themes that have a key role to play in tectonic hazard mitigation over the next 10–15 years.

Reconfiguring the global challenge – disaster reduction in the 1990s

During the 1980s there was growing international consensus that something had to be done to try to reduce escalating susceptibility to human and economic losses from natural hazard impacts. This led the General Assembly of the United Nations to declare, in December 1989, that the 1990s would be an International Decade for Natural Disaster Reduction (IDNDR), through which concerted international action would be aimed at reducing the social and economic disruption caused by natural hazards, particularly in developing countries. The initial goals of the decade, as set out in UN Resolution 42/169, were:

- to improve the capacity of countries, particularly poor ones, to mitigate the effects of natural disasters, paying particular attention to developing early warning systems and disaster resistant structures
- to devise guidelines and strategies for applying existing scientific and technical knowledge
- to foster scientific and engineering endeavours aimed at closing critical gaps in knowledge
- to disseminate existing and new technical information related to measures for the assessment, prediction and mitigation of natural disasters
- to assist developing countries in all of the above through programmes of technical assistance and technology transfer.

The reasoning behind these goals is not hard to appreciate. Significant hazard impacts in developing countries during the 1980s, including the 1985 Mexico City earthquake and the Nevado del Ruiz volcanic eruption in Colombia, had exacted horrific human death tolls, whereas major hazard impacts in developed countries (e.g. the 1980 Mount St Helen's volcanic eruption and the 1989 Loma Prieta earthquake in California) had caused major economic loss and disruption but killed relatively few people. This concern was compounded by a growing realisation of the implications of rapid rates of population growth and, in particular, urbanisation for exposure to natural hazards in developing countries. The map in Figure 1.5 is from one of a number of studies from the early 1990s that demonstrated growing global exposure to tectonic hazards through rapid urbanisation in the developing world. Figure 6.1 is derived from analysis of the hazard exposure of the cities in the map, and emphasises that the switch (1970s–) in the focus of world urbanisation from the richer countries of the global north to poorer ones of the south was accompanied by a discernable increase in global risk, because many of the largest cities in the south are situated in more hazardous environments than their counterparts in the north. In Figure 6.1 the modal rank hazard exposure for the largest cities of developing countries is 3, but 0 for those of developed countries.

The assumption, implicit in the initial goals of the UN IDNDR, was that this global escalation of risk could be managed though scientific, engineering and technical endeavours aimed at improving societies' capacity to predict and control hazards. Such methods (see Figure 6.2) were characteristic of the environmentally deterministic paradigm of disaster management that dominated the age (see Information Box 1.3). They had been pivotal to reducing the loss of life from hazard impacts in rich

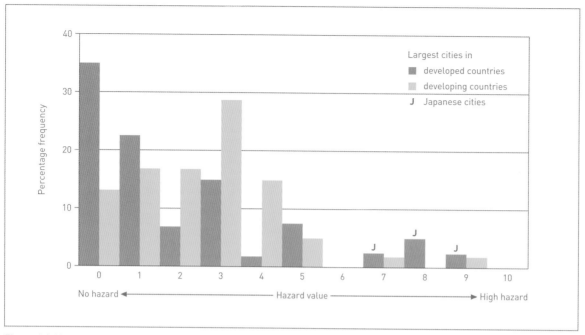

Figure 6.1 Hazard exposure ratings of the largest cities of developed and developing countries. **Source:** after Degg, 1992.

countries, and key proponents of the IDNDR felt that the benefits of this western expertise should now be transferred to poorer countries of the south through technical aid programmes. Social scientists, including human geographers, were quick to point out the lack of reference to human causes of disaster in the UN objectives. They pressed for a more rounded view of disaster, akin to that presented in the alternative paradigm (Information Box 1.3) of disasters generally and the PAR model (Information Box 1.1 and Figure 1.4) in particular, with equal emphasis on measures to tackle the social, economic and political processes that create conditions of vulnerability (V) within human societies (Blaikie *et al.*, 1994; Varley, 1994). Why spend yet more money on research into hazard (H) processes, they argued, when fundamental problems such as human overcrowding of dilapidated structures situated on marginal land (see Figure 6.3) create conditions of abject vulnerability to hazard for millions of people in cities of the developing world? So persuasive were their arguments that, by

Figure 6.2 Scientist monitoring earthquake hazard in western Idaho, USA. **Photo:** Idaho National Laboratory/ Flickr (Creative Commons licence).

the mid-point of the decade, the UN objectives had been redefined to place increased emphasis on tackling vulnerability alongside hazard as equal components in the construction of disaster risk.

With this rebalancing of the global risk reduction agenda through the 1990s came a growing acceptance that greater emphasis needed to be placed on small-scale, community initiatives. Technical interventions to manage hazard

had tended, by their very nature, to be top-down – i.e. centrally controlled and administered, involving relatively large budgets, (western) experts, consultants and so on. Ordinary people were often not involved in the process at all, and there is a strong sense of this in the objectives of the decade listed above. The vulnerability agenda, in contrast, placed greater emphasis on the importance of small-scale interventions involving

Figure 6.3 Rocincha *favela* (shanty town) on the slopes of Rio de Janeiro, Brazil.
Photo: Alicia Nijdam/Flickr (Creative Commons licence).

individual citizens and small community groups in bottom-up or community-based hazard mitigation and disaster reduction initiatives (Maskrey, 1989).

Tectonic hazard impact and disaster reduction at the start of a new century

Those originally involved in proposing the IDNDR could be forgiven for looking at the global record of tectonic hazard impact from the first decade of the 21st century with a tangible sense of disappointment. It has, by any measure, been a terribly catastrophic 10-year period. Earthquake impacts, such as the 2005 (M=7.6) earthquake in Kashmir that levelled more than 30,000 buildings, killing more than 70,000 people, and the 2010 (M=7.0) event in Haiti that killed more than 200,000 people and made some 2 million Haitians homeless (20% of the country's population), have served to emphasise the continued levels of vulnerability to tectonic hazard of many millions of people in poor countries (*National Geographic*, 2010). Elsewhere events in the developed world, such as the 2010 eruption of Eyjafjallajökull in a remote part of Iceland in the North

Atlantic, have provided a stark demonstration of the escalating vulnerability of an increasingly interconnected and technologically dependent globalised society to inordinate levels of disruption and economic loss caused by moderate hazard impacts.

Beyond these events, there have been the truly great tectonic incidents of the last 10 years (see Figure 3.2), most particularly the 2004 Sumatran earthquake (M=9.1) and associated Indian Ocean tsunami that killed more than 230,000 people, and the 2011 Sendai earthquake (M=9.0) and tsunami along the north-east coast of Japan, which killed approximately 20,000 people. Both of these can be argued to be global hazard impacts from a number of perspectives. To begin with, images of the events, in particular the unfolding tsunami tragedies, were broadcast live into homes in every country around the world, so that people of all ages and races witnessed first-hand the awesome power of the forces at work, the trauma of the people affected, and the stark realities of the powerlessness of humanity in some of the poorer countries on the planet, as well as in one of the richest and most technologically

advanced. They were also global events in terms of their impact and the response they generated. The Indian Ocean tsunami impacted most directly on 11 countries of South Asia, the Middle East and East Africa, but the victims of the tsunami included several thousand holidaymakers from more than 40 different countries. For example, the European country most affected was Sweden (543 deaths or 58 fatalities per million inhabitants) because of the large numbers of Swedish tourists on holiday in coastal resorts of South Asia for the Christmas vacation of 2004. The immediate impact of the 2011 Japanese tsunami was more tightly concentrated within Japan itself, and along the north-east coast of the island of Honshu in particular, but the global dimensions included concerns about the implications of the anticipated US$200–300 billion economic loss for the global economy and worries about possible radioactive contamination emanating from a nuclear power plant crippled in the event.

A number of important disaster management themes have emerged strongly through the losses of the first decade of this century, two of which might at first glance appear to be diametrically opposed. The first is a reminder that modern technology has a pivotal role to play in reducing vulnerability to tectonic hazards. The second is a growing realisation that traditional (indigenous) knowledge and expertise can be key to sustainable hazard mitigation over the longer term. The importance of the former was aptly displayed by the Indian Ocean tsunami disaster, and in particular by the lack of a tsunami warning system (and associated emergency response procedures) for the Indian Ocean comparable to that which has operated very effectively in the Pacific since the 1960s in reducing the loss of life from tsunami. The international community is working to address this, and the first Indian Ocean seafloor sensors were installed in 2006. This same disaster highlighted the importance of lay knowledge (i.e. knowledge and understanding that is held by non-experts) in responding quickly and effectively to hazard to save lives. For example, on the island of Simeulue situated off the coast of Sumatra and within 100km of the earthquake epicentre (see Figure 4.6), only seven people out of a total population of 83,000 were killed by the tsunami. This was because the islanders had maintained folklore knowledge about earthquakes experienced in the past, with each generation reminding the next that, if the sea goes out following an earthquake, you should move to higher ground because a tsunami is coming. Meanwhile, on the mainland of Sumatra just 100km away, this knowledge had either never existed or had been lost through time, with the result that the tsunami killed over 150,000 people because they failed to appreciate the danger and evacuate low-lying coastal areas in time (Greenhough et al., 2005; Keller and Blodgett, 2008).

These themes are reflected in the current UN International Strategy for Disaster Reduction (ISDR) and associated Hyogo Framework for Action (HFA), 2005–15 (www.unisdr.org/hfa). The priorities within the HFA reflect just how much the international disaster mitigation agenda has moved forward from the early days of the IDNDR in 1990. Key priorities today include:

- collaboration to ensure disaster risk reduction is a national and local priority
- identifying, assessing and monitoring disaster risk, and enhanced early warning
- use of knowledge and education to build a culture of safety and resilience at all levels
- reduction of underlying social and environmental risk factors
- strengthened disaster preparedness at all levels.

Note the emphasis on disaster risk, with risk viewed as the product of hazard and vulnerability (see Information Box 1.1). Note also the emphasis on collaboration rather than on knowledge transfer from north to south, and the acceptance that local knowledge can be just as important to disaster reduction as the views of experts. Finally, note the references to cultures of safety and community and individual *resilience* – the realisation that resistance to hazard often has to come from within individual, family and community daily actions, rather than through strategies and methods that are imposed from above/outside. Indeed, the video that the UN produced to promote ISDR argues that disaster mitigation is 'everybody's business'. We explore what this means in practical terms for citizens of rich and poor countries exposed to tectonic hazards in the next and final section of the book.

Future challenges – making tectonic disaster mitigation everybody's business to build cultures of prevention

The 2011 Sendai earthquake and tsunami disaster in Japan provided a stark illustration of people's continuing vulnerability to tectonic hazards, and a reminder that this vulnerability embraces some of the richest and most technologically advanced countries in the world as well as many of the poorest. Indeed it might be argued that aspects of Japan's technological sophistication served to compound and prolong the effects of the Sendai earthquake, not least through the damage caused to nuclear power stations.

The disaster risk reduction challenge facing rich and poor countries today is fundamentally the same: how to deliver sustainable reductions in vulnerability to loss in areas of tectonic hazard exposure that are congested with people living in built environments that are increasingly complex and sensitive

to disruption from even the most moderate of hazard impacts. At a global level the number of people and the economic value of assets at risk are of staggering proportions, such that it has become more and more apparent that there is a limit to what can be achieved through centralised government actions to reduce risk, not least because of the cost implications. Clearly disaster risk reduction has to find ways of engaging ordinary people in the hazard mitigation process (Huppert and Sparks, 2006; Shah, 2006).

There are some very good examples of this type of activity from developed and developing countries, operating at various levels within societies and involving a range of activities and methods. Some of the most heavily publicised efforts have been government-led awareness-raising programmes in developed countries, such as that which operates in Japan generally, and in Tokyo in particular (Mitchell, 1999). This includes, among other things, a national Disaster Preparedness Day held every year on the anniversary of the great Tokyo/Kanto earthquake of 1923. The main purpose of the day is to involve the emergency services and general public in preparing for natural disasters. Part of the emphasis is on rehearsing what to do in the event of a major hazard impact (emergency disaster response), but there is also a focus on the small but important proactive steps that can be taken by individuals and family and community groups to reduce collective vulnerability to hazards (disaster mitigation) – for example, fixing bookcases to walls so they are less likely to fall on people in an earthquake, and changing daily cooking practices so there is less chance of fires being started by cooking stoves knocked over in an earthquake. The importance of the latter small but important adaptation to the way in which people live their daily lives, in a country whose capital was ravaged by earthquake-triggered firestorms in 1923 killing 150,000 people, is summarised in the following quote from two leading earthquake engineers: 'The type of cooking stove a family uses, and their awareness that a sudden earthquake could tip it over is more important in reducing the risk of conflagration than the community maintaining a large fire brigade' (Coburn and Spence, 2002).

In other contexts, community-based risk reduction programmes involve building on established traditions going back many generations to foster cultures of prevention. Such indigenous responses, like the tsunami hazard awareness described above that exists among the islanders of Simeuleu off the coast of Sumatra, appear to have characterised many parts of the world in the past, but all too often have been lost or weakened in recent centuries through the development process and associated effects of rapid urbanisation (population shifts), modernisation and globalisation (Jackson, 2006; Halvorson and Parker Hamilton, 2007). For example, the high death toll in the 2005 Kashmir earthquake was largely attributable to inadequately designed and constructed buildings made from modern building materials like concrete. The expertise needed to build earthquake-resistant structures from such materials had not been commonly available in the region in the decades leading up to the earthquake. Meanwhile, buildings constructed using traditional methods such as Dhajji Dewari and Taq (see Figure 6.4), in which frames of horizontal, vertical and diagonal timbers are used to tie earthen and masonry walls together to give ductility and resist shearing earthquake ground motions (see Chapter 3), performed much better. Clearly there is much to be gained in this type of social and environmental setting from blending the old with the new – taking traditional building practices and

adapting them to facilitate the use of new building materials.

Elsewhere the challenge is to seek to establish cultures of prevention where there is little sense of them ever having existed in the past. The Middle Eastern region, for example, is a part of the world in which human life seems extremely exposed to the risk from earthquakes (Degg and Homan, 2005; Halvorson and Parker Hamilton, 2007). Figure 6.5 demonstrates the horrific death tolls associated with recent medium and strong earthquakes in this part of the Alpine–Himalayan continental collision

zone, particularly in comparison to human losses experienced in North American earthquakes of comparable magnitude. One of the principal reasons for this is traditional building practices, particularly in rural areas, where houses are typically constructed of thick earthen (adobe) walls with heavy timber and earthen roofs to provide insulation in hot summers and cold winters. Such stiff structures have little resistance to earthquake shearing motions, and so crumble, trapping people under heavy walls and roof timbers and creating a suffocating dust (see Figure 6.6). For example,

Figure 6.4 Dhajji Dewari – an earthquake-resistant building practice. **Source:** UNESCO.

in the Bam (Iran) earthquake of 2003, 85% of the city's buildings collapsed, killing 30,000 people and injuring a further 30,000. The solution to this problem need not be as daunting as at first appears, if people can be enabled to help themselves in the risk reduction process. For example, Figure 6.7 is a builder training programme introduced into the Yemen Arab Republic following a catastrophic earthquake. In a single sheet of A4 paper it shows local people how to construct an earthquake-resistant house using traditional materials and skills. The hope is that if one generation of builders is taught how to do this the knowledge and understanding will then be passed on to the next generation, leading to the establishment of a culture of prevention. This approach to disaster risk reduction is sustainable in every sense of the word – economically, environmentally and socially, as well as in terms of longevity.

Such an approach also necessitates a new type of relationship between the expert professional and the lay person. The specialist knowledge of scientists (e.g. seismologists, volcanologists, oceanographers), engineers and hazard planners has to be presented in ways that are accessible and meaningful to the ordinary man, woman and child on the street (Degg and Homan, 2005). Note, for example, that there is very little writing in Figure 6.7, thereby increasing its meaning to communities where many people involved in house building will not be able to read. The same expert professionals, when they are responsible for overseeing the safe location and construction of engineered buildings and infrastructure (e.g. schools, hospitals, roads, power plants, tenement blocks) within hazardous areas, must be held more accountable for their decisions and actions if standards are not met (Shah, 2006). As our example from Egypt in Chapter 3 showed (Figure 3.12), building codes and land-use planning regulations are only as effective as the measures that are taken to ensure that they are implemented.

Conclusion

The international disaster mitigation agenda has progressed significantly over the last 20 years, from an emphasis on the top-down application of specialist science and technology to try to predict and control environmental threats in the early 1990s, to an emphasis on promoting the benefits of social and political preparedness to increase individual and community resilience to hazard impacts. Central to the current agenda is the need to engage each and every person, consciously or subconsciously, in the hazard mitigation process, and key to this is the need to make specialist knowledge about hazard mitigation more accessible and meaningful to ordinary men, women and children in their daily lives – i.e. to break down barriers between the expert and the lay person. Geographers have an important contribution to make to this process because they, arguably, are best placed to communicate the interplay of human and physical factors and processes that go to make up risky situations and disaster scenarios.

Year	Location	Magnitude	Fatalities	Damage (US$ millions)
1980	El Asnam, Algeria	7.2	2590	3000
1982	Dhamar, Yemen AR	5.7	1900	218
1990	Rasht/Gilan Province, Iran	7.4	40,000	7100
1992	Erzincan, Turkey	6.8	540	750
1992	Dahshur, Egypt	5.6	561	1200
1997	Ardabil, Iran	5.5	800	–
1999	Izmit, Turkey	7.4	17,225	12,000
1999	Düzce, Turkey	7.1	845	500
2003	Bam, Iran	6.5	30,000	–
2005	Kashmir, NE Pakistan	7.6	73,000	
1979	*Imperial Valley, USA*	6.6	0	30
1989	*Loma Prieta, USA*	7.1	68	6000
1994	*Northridge, USA*	6.8	61	44,000

Figure 6.5 Recent earthquake disasters in the Middle East, with losses from some North American earthquakes for comparison.
Source: after Degg and Homan, 2005.

Politicians and leaders must take the initiative in convincing people that it is better to spend money on measures that lead to greater resilience to disaster than to spend it on emergency disaster relief. This is not straightforward, because it requires people to take a longer-term perspective on the merits of such actions, and to accept that their benefits may not be apparent within individual lifetimes, if at all. As Kofi Annan, Secretary General of the UN, observed in 1999: 'Building a culture of prevention is not easy. While the costs of prevention have to be paid in the present, its benefits lie in a distant future. Moreover, the benefits are not tangible; they are the disasters that did not happen' (Annan, 1999).

Figure 6.6 Earthquake damage to typical Middle Eastern two-to-three-storey non-engineered dwellings of timber and mud (adobe) brick construction, northern Nile valley, Egypt. **Photo:** Martin Degg.

Figure 6.7 Improved (earthquake-resistant) building construction techniques promoted through a self-help builder training information sheet from the Yemen Arab Republic. Note the use of keystones and timber straps to tie vertical and horizontal structural elements of the building together to give greater resistance to earthquake shear. The Arabic numerals show the appropriate mixture of sand, cement and water to make a strong mortar. **Source:** after Leslie, as reproduced in Coburn and Spence, 2002.

ACTIVITY BOX 6

1 The 2010 Haiti earthquake was a mega-disaster that killed over 250,000 people. Research the reasons why the numbers killed were so high, and why all stages of necessary reconstruction have been beset with problems.

2 Summarise how and why the international disaster mitigation agenda has changed over the last 20 years. How do you think it will change in the future?

3 Design a public information sheet like that in Figure 6.7 to reduce the vulnerability of schoolchildren to earthquake hazard in a school in a country of your choice. You will need to research the particular characteristics of the earthquake hazard in your chosen country and factors that make children more/less vulnerable to earthquake hazard in a classroom setting.

 Extra resources to accompany this chapter are available on the Top Spec web pages. See page 4 for further information.

References

Annan, K. (1999) *Facing the Humanitarian Challenge: Towards a culture of prevention*. New York: United Nations. Available online at *http://desastres.usac.edu.gt/documents/pdf/eng/dec/2226/doc12226.htm* (last accessed 21 November 2011).

Blaikie, P., Cannon, T., Davis, I. and Wisner, B. (1994) *At Risk: Natural hazards, people's vulnerability and disaster*. London: Routledge.

Coburn, A. and Spence, R. (2002) *Earthquake Protection* (2nd edition). Chichester: Wiley.

Degg, M.R. (1992) 'Natural disasters: recent trends and future prospects', *Geography*, 77, 3, pp. 198–209.

Degg, M.R. and Homan, J. (2005) 'Earthquake vulnerability in the Middle East', *Geography*, 90, 1, pp. 54–66.

Greenhough, B., Jazeel, T. and Massey, D. (2005) 'Geographical encounters with the Indian Ocean tsunami', *The Geographical Journal*, 171, 4, pp. 369–71.

Halvorson, S.J. and Parker Hamilton, J. (2007) 'Vulnerability and the erosion of seismic culture in mountainous Central Asia', *Mountain Research and Development*, 27, 4, pp. 322–30.

Huppert, H.E. and Sparks, R.S.J. (2006) 'Extreme natural hazards: population growth, globalization and environmental change', *Philosophical Transactions of the Royal Society A*, 364, pp.1875–88.

Jackson, J. (2006) 'Fatal attraction: Living with earthquakes, the growth of villages into megacities, and earthquake vulnerability in the modern world', *Philosophical Transactions of the Royal Society A*, 364, pp.1911–25.

Keller, E.A. and Blodgett, R.H. (2008) *Natural Hazards: Earth's processes as hazards, disasters and catastrophes* (2nd edition). London: Pearson.

Maskrey, A. (1989) *Disaster Mitigation: A community based approach*. Oxford: Oxfam.

Mitchell, J.K. (ed.) (1999) *Crucibles of Hazard: Mega-cities and disasters in transition*. Tokyo: UNU.

National Geographic (2010) *Nature's Fury: Inside today's disasters*. Special Issue.

Shah, H.C. (2006) 'The last mile: earthquake risk mitigation assistance in developing countries', *Philosophical Transactions of the Royal Society A*, 364, pp. 2183–9.

United Nations International Strategy for Disaster Reduction (2005) *Hyogo Framework for Action*. Available online at *www.unisdr.org/hfa* (last accessed 12 May 2011).

Varley, A. (ed.) (1994), *Disasters, Development and Environment*. Chichester: Wiley.

Key terms

Active landscape: area where plate motion is contributing to the formation of tectonic landforms within a wider physical landscape today.

Alternative paradigm: school of thought that sees natural disasters as consequences of socio-political processes that constrain people and make them vulnerable; also known as the socially deterministic or structural paradigm.

Andesitic volcanoes: explosive volcanoes which erupt intermediate andesitic lava, ash and gas.

Aseismic: designed to withstand earthquake activity.

Asthenosphere: a zone within the Earth's upper mantle, extending from 50km to around 700km deep and considered to be the zone over which the relatively rigid lithosphere moves causing movement of the tectonic plates.

Caldera: a large, roughly circular volcanic structure, usually formed by the collapse of land following a volcanic eruption.

Compressional wave (P-wave): a type of earthquake wave which shakes the ground in the direction of wave travel; the fastest seismic wave, the first to be detected and the least destructive.

Constructive margins: occur where two plates slide apart from each other. Within continents, they initially produce rifts which later lead to rift valleys. The most active constructive plate boundaries occur between oceanic plates and exist as mid-oceanic ridges. They also form volcanic islands which occur when the plates move apart, producing gaps that are filled by rising molten lava.

Contintental crust: the oldest crust consisting of low-density granitic material and between 25km and 75km thick.

Crust: uppermost layer of the lithosphere.

Deep ocean assessment and reporting of tsunami (DART) buoys: component of an enhanced tsunami warning system. Each DART station consists of a surface buoy and a seafloor bottom pressure recording (BPR) package that detects pressure changes caused by tsunami.

Destructive margins: occur where two plates slide towards each other, commonly forming either a subduction zone (if one plate moves underneath the other) or a continental collision (if the two plates contain continental crust).

Disaster: the realisation of risk.

Dominant paradigm: school of thought that sees natural disasters primarily as consequences of environmental processes, compounded by inappropriate human actions in the face of such threats due to ignorance/lack of awareness; also known as the environmentally deterministic or behavioural paradigm.

Drawback: phenomenon that often occurs before a tsunami, where water along the shoreline recedes dramatically, exposing normally submerged areas. Occurs if the first part of a tsunami to reach land is a trough rather than a wave crest.

Epicentre: the point on the Earth's surface which lies directly above the focus (origin) of an earthquake.

Extensometer: a device for measuring the deformation of material under stress.

Hazard: potentially damaging event that may cause loss of life, property damage, social and economic disruption or environmental degradation.

Hot spot: where an isolated column of hot mantle material rises beneath a tectonic plate.

Intensity (I): a descriptive measure of the effects of earthquake shaking on people, structures and the surface of the Earth. Denoted using Roman numerals, e.g. I to XII.

International Decade for Natural Disaster Reduction (IDNDR): UN programme that aimed to decrease the loss of life, property destruction and social and economic disruption caused by natural disasters and ran between 1990 and 2000. Succeeded by the International Strategy for Disaster Reduction (ISDR), 2005–15.

Intraplate: within a plate, rather than at a plate boundary (interplate).

Island arc systems: type of archipelago composed of an arc-shaped chain of volcanoes, which are situated parallel and close to a boundary between two converging tectonic plates.

Lahar: destructive mudflow on the slopes of a volcano.

Large igneous province (LIP): an extremely large accumulation of igneous rocks – either intrusive, extrusive or both – found in the Earth's crust. Created by periodic episodes of enhanced volcanic activity throughout geological time.

Liquefaction: the process by which water-saturated sediments lose cohesion and behave like a fluid during strong earthquake ground shaking.

Lithosphere: outermost layer of the solid earth, broken up into numerous tectonic plates, or lithospheric plates, both oceanic and continental in composition.

Low velocity zone (LVZ): zone that occurs between about 80km and 300km depth, close to the boundary between the lithosphere and the asthenosphere in the upper mantle. It is characterised by unusually low seismic shear wave velocity compared to the surrounding depth intervals.

Magma: hot liquid rock material within the Earth's crust from which lava and other igneous rock is formed by cooling.

Mantle: the region of the Earth's interior between the crust and the core.

Mega-city: city with a population of over 10 million people.

Microzonation: process of subdividing a potentially earthquake-prone area into zones with respect to some geological and geophysical characteristics of the sites such as ground shaking, liquefaction susceptibility, landslide and rock fall hazard, and earthquake-related flooding, so that seismic hazards at different locations within the area can be correctly identified.

Mitigate: make less serious or severe.

Moment magnitude (M): a measure of the size of an earthquake based on the amount of energy released.

Morphology: form, shape.

Natural hazard: potentially damaging natural physical event that may cause loss of life, property damage, social and economic disruption, or environmental degradation.

Oceanic crust: crust formed continually at constructive plate margins.

Orogenic (mountain) belt: a mountain range formed by the compression of the earth's crust due to a collision between tectonic plates.

Pacific Ring of Fire: a 40,000-km (25,000-mile) horseshoe-shaped area around the Pacific basin associated with a nearly continuous series of oceanic trenches, volcanic arcs and volcanic belts and/or plate movements. Home to over 75% of the world's active and dormant volcanoes. Also known as the circum-Pacific belt or the circum-Pacific seismic belt.

Paradigm: example, model or pattern.

Precursor: something that comes before another.

Pyroclastic flow: fast-moving current of superheated gas and tephra that can flow from an erupting volcano. Can reach temperatures of 1000°C and speeds of up to 700 km/h (450 mph).

Relict landscape: area where tectonic activity has happened in the past but no longer occurs; now usually weathered and eroded.

Resilience: ability to withstand or recover from difficult conditions.

Rift system: occurs when tectonic plates pull apart, leading to crustal extension. Characterised by: linear mountain ranges (ridges); a central rift within the ridge; lakes (or as the rift opens, the sea); numerous relatively small basaltic volcanic eruptions generating cinder cones, larger volcanoes and lava flows; dykes.

Risk: the probability of harmful consequences or expected losses resulting from interactions between natural or human-induced hazards and vulnerable people/conditions.

Run-up height: the maximum onshore water height of a wave above sea level.

Seismic wave: energy pulses which travel through the Earth in the form of waves as a result of an earthquake.

Seismometer: an instrument that measures and records physical characteristics of earthquakes such as ground motion and duration.

Shear waves (S-waves): secondary seismic waves, which are detected after P-waves and have a lower velocity. They cause ground motion perpendicular to the direction of wave travel.

Stratigraphy: the branch of geology concerned with the study of the layers of rock in the Earth's surface.

Stratovolcano: tall, conical volcano built up of many layers of hardened lava, tephra, pumice and volcanic ash.

Subduction: the sideways and downwards movement of the edge of the Earth's (oceanic) crust into the mantle beneath another plate.

Techno-fix: attempting to reduce the impact of a hazard by using technology and engineering either to predict the event or to prevent its consequences.

Tectonic hazard: hazard related to changes in or movements of the structure of the Earth's crust.

Tectonic plate: piece of the Earth's crust and uppermost mantle.

Tephra: rock fragments and particles ejected by a volcanic eruption.

Tsunami: large and potentially devastating waves in oceans, seas and occasionally lakes.

Tsunamigenic: a sub-sea earthquake which generates a tsunami due to vertical displacement of the seabed. Not all sub-sea earthquakes are tsunamigenic.

Viscous: having a thick, sticky consistency between solid and liquid.

Volcanic explosivity index (VEI): scale that provides a relative measure of the explosiveness of volcanic eruptions. Volume of products, eruption cloud height and qualitative observations (using terms ranging from 'non-explosive' to 'mega-colossal') are used to determine the explosivity value. The scale is open-ended, with the largest volcanoes in history being given magnitude 8.

Vulnerability: susceptibility to loss (death, injury, property, livelihood, disruption to economic activity or environmental damage) caused by a hazard impact.